Bill Kuhn
1985

D0030577

Glory & Praise

Glory & Praise

Parish Music Program

North American Liturgy Resources • Phoenix, Arizona 85029.

© 1977, 1980, 1983, 1984 by North American Liturgy Resources, Phoenix, Arizona 85029. All rights reserved.

The English translation of The Rite of Marriage © 1969, International Committee on English in the Liturgy, Inc., (ICEL); the English translation of The Rite of Baptism for Children © 1969, ICEL; the English translation of The Rite of Funerals © 1970 ICEL; the English translation of The Roman Missal © 1973 ICEL. All rights reserved.

Notices of copyright ownership of the individual songs are printed below each song. Neither text nor music may be copied or reprinted by any means without the express written permission of North American Liturgy Resources (NALR), a division of Epoch Universal Publications, Inc., 10802 N. 23rd Ave., Phoenix, Arizona 85029.

In Canada: NALR/Epoch Universal Publications, Ltd., 6315 Shawson Dr., Suite 17, Mississauga, Ontario L5T 1J2.

Table of Contents

Other GLORY & PRAISE resources:

GLORY & PRAISE, VOLUME 1; song numbers 1 to 80.

Songbook, melody / lyric	GP1-COM-SB
Guitar Accompaniment	GP1-COM-GT
Keyboard Accompaniment	GP1-COM-KB
Stereo LP Set	GP1-COM-LP
Stereo Cassette Set	GP1-COM-CS

GLORY & PRAISE, VOLUME 2; song numbers 81 to 173

Songbook, melody / lyric	GP2-COM-SB
Guitar Accompaniment	GP2-COM-GT
Keyboard Accompaniment	GP2-COM-KB
Stereo LP Set	GP2-COM-LP
Stereo Cassette Set	GP2-COM-CS

GLORY & PRAISE, VOLUME 3; song numbers 174 to 275

Songbook, melody / lyric	GP3-COM-SB
Guitar Accompaniment	GP3-COM-GT
Keyboard Accompaniment	GP3-COM-KB
Stereo LP Set	GP3-COM-LP
Stereo Cassette Set	GP3-COM-CS

GLORY & PRAISE LEADER'S GUIDE GPLGN-COM-BK

YOUNG PEOPLE'S GLORY & PRAISE

Songbook, melody / lyric	GPYP-COM-SB
Guitar Accompaniment	GPYP-COM-GT
Keyboard Accompaniment	GPYP-COM-KB
Stereo Cassette Set	GPYP-COM-CS

The above resources plus many more are available at your local religious goods bookstore or directly from the publisher, NALR, 10802 N. 23rd Ave., Phoenix, Arizona 85029.

Introduction

There are many reasons that people gather, and many places that they gather in. But the coming together of people in this place, is special. For the people who gather here, come together as people gathered in the Lord's name.

Over the past years, our society has tended to put much emphasis on the individual person. This has been helpful in coming to understand the uniqueness and giftedness of each person. It has also been helpful in reminding us of the need that we each have of a personal faith relationship with our Lord. But at the same time, it can be harmful if it breaks down the relationships that we must have with each other, with the Church.

Liturgy, which is what we are gathered here for, is a common expression of faith. It is based on a Greek word which can best be defined as a "public work done for the service of others". Liturgy, or public worship, is not meant as our one time a week with God. It is not meant to be a time of private prayer, although prayerfulness is essential to common worship. It is meant to be a time when we come together, as *one* people, to publically proclaim the Word, proclaim our faith, and share in the Body of Christ.

We are here as a ministry. Each of us, not simply the celebrant and the people sitting in the sanctuary, but all of us are here by our presence and by our participation for the purpose of ministering to one another. We need to support, and be supported by each other. The Scriptures tell us that "where two or three are gathered, there am I in their midsts."

This worship aid, **Glory & Praise**, has been created to help your community give fitting, beautiful, and public praise to our God. It is our hope, that it will be one assistance to you in offering the gift of yourself to our God and to each other. But, the faith of this community needs to bring these words and these notes to life.

It is our hope and our prayer, that your community may truly be on fire with the love of God, and that you may offer *Glory and Praise to our God.*

Special thanks to

Peter C. Finn,
Assistant to the Executive Secretary, ICEL;

*for his kind assistance and advice in development of this
Order of Mass, Rite of Baptism, Rite of Marriage
and Rite of Funerals.*

Order of
Mass

Introductory Rites

Entrance Song
Greeting

> Celebrant: In the name of the Father, and of the Son, and of the Holy Spirit.

> All: Amen.

> A. Celebrant: The grace of our Lord Jesus Christ and the love of God and the fellowship of the Holy Spirit be with you all.

> All: And also with you.

> B. Celebrant: The grace and peace of God our Father and the Lord Jesus be with you.

> All: And also with you.

> C. Celebrant: The Lord be with you.

> All: And also with you.

Penitential Rite

> A. All: I confess to almighty God
> and to you, my brothers and sisters,
> that I have sinned through my own fault,
> in my thoughts and in my words,
> in what I have done,
> and in what I have failed to do;
> and I ask blessed Mary, ever virgin,
> all the angels and saints,
> and you, my brothers and sisters,
> to pray for me to the Lord our God.

> Celebrant: May almighty God have mercy on us,
> forgive us our sins,
> and bring us to life everlasting.

> All: Amen.

> Celebrant: Lord, have mercy.
> All: Lord, have mercy.

2

| Celebrant: | Christ, have mercy. |
| All: | Christ, have mercy. |

| Celebrant: | Lord, have mercy. |
| All: | Lord, have mercy. |

B. Celebrant: Lord, we have sinned against you.

All: Lord, have mercy.

Celebrant: Lord, show us your mercy and love.

All: And grant us your salvation.

Celebrant: *(Words of absolution)*

All: Amen.

C. Celebrant:
*(or other
minister)*
(Invocation), Lord, have mercy.

All: Lord, have mercy.

Celebrant· *(Invocation), Christ, have mercy.*

All: Christ, have mercy.

Celebrant: *(Invocation), Lord, have mercy.*

All: Lord, have mercy.

Celebrant: *(Words of absolution)*

All: Amen.

The Rite of Blessing and Sprinkling Holy Water

(This rite may be used in place of the Penitential Rite; this rite reminds each of his/her call in baptism. If used, this rite follows the **Greeting** and is concluded with the following prayer:)

Celebrant: *May almighty God cleanse us of our sins, and through the eucharist we celebrate make us worthy to sit at his table in his heavenly kingdom.*

All: Amen.

3

Gloria

All: Glory to God in the highest,
and peace to his people on earth.
Lord God, heavenly King,
almighty God and Father,
  we worship you,
  we give you thanks,
  we praise you for your glory.
Lord Jesus Christ,
only Son of the Father,
Lord God, Lamb of God,
you take away the sin of the world:
  have mercy on us;
you are seated at the right hand
of the Father:
  receive our prayer.
For you alone are the Holy One,
you alone are the Lord,
you alone are the Most High,
Jesus Christ,
with the Holy Spirit,
in the glory of God the Father.
Amen.

Opening Prayer

All: Amen

Liturgy of the Word

First Reading

Lector: This is the Word of the Lord.

All: Thanks be to God.
(short period of silent reflection)

Responsorial Psalm

The cantor sings the response, and all repeat it. After the cantor sings each verse of the psalm, all repeat the response.

Second Reading

Lector: This is the Word of the Lord.

All: Thanks be to God.

(short period of silent reflection)

Gospel Acclamation

The cantor or choir intones the Alleluia.

During Lent, the sung acclamation is Glory and praise to you, Lord Jesus Christ or some other Lenten acclamation.

Gospel

Celebrant:
(or other
minister)

The is the Gospel of the Lord.

All: Praise to you, Lord Jesus Christ.

Homily

Profession of Faith (Nicene Creed)

All: We believe in one God,
the Father, the Almighty,
maker of heaven and earth,
of all that is seen and unseen.

We believe in one Lord, Jesus Christ.
the only Son of God,
eternally begotten of the Father,
God from God, Light from Light,
true God from true God,
begotten, not made, one in Being with the Father.
Through him, all things were made.
For us men and for our salvation
he came down from heaven:
by the power of the Holy Spirit
he was born of the Virgin Mary, and became man.

For our sake he was crucified under Pontius Pilate;
he suffered, died, and was buried.

5

On the third day he rose again
  in fulfillment of the Scriptures;
 he ascended into heaven
  and is seated at the right hand of the Father.
 He will come again in glory
  to judge the living and the dead,
 and his kingdom will have no end.

We believe in the Holy Spirit, the Lord, the giver of life.
 Who proceeds from the Father and the Son.
 With the Father and the Son he is worshiped and glorified
 He has spoken through the Prophets.
 We believe in the holy catholic and apostolic Church.
 We acknowledge one baptism for the forgiveness of sins.
 We look for the resurrection of the dead,
  and the life of the world to come. Amen.

General Intercessions (Prayer of the Faithful)

To each intercession all respond: Lord, hear our prayer, or some other response. The Celebrant concludes the intercessions with a prayer.

> All: Amen.

Liturgy of the Eucharist

Preparation of the Altar and the Gifts - Procession with the Gifts

> Celebrant: *Blessed are you, Lord, God of all creation.*
> *Through your goodness*

> we have this bread to offer,
> which earth has given
> and human hands have made.
> It will become for us the bread of life.

All: Blessed be God for ever.

Celebrant: Blessed are you, Lord, God of all creation.
Through your goodness
we have this wine to offer,
fruit of the vine and work of human hands.
It will become our spiritual drink.

All: Blessed be God for ever.

Invitation to Prayer by the Priest Celebrant

All: May the Lord accept the sacrifice at your hands
for the praise and glory of his name,
for our good, and the good of all his Church.

Prayer Over the Gifts

All: Amen

Eucharistic Prayer

Preface

Celebrant: The Lord be with you.
All: And also with you.

Celebrant: Lift up your hearts.
All: We lift them up to the Lord.

Celebrant: Let us give thanks
to the Lord our God.
All: It is right to give him thanks
and praise.

Acclamation

All: Holy, holy, holy Lord,
God of power and might,

7

heaven and earth
are full of your glory.
  Hosanna in the highest.
  Blessed is he who comes
in the name of the Lord.
  Hosanna in the highest.

Memorial Acclamation

Celebrant
(or deacon): *Let us proclaim the mystery of faith.*
A. All: Christ has died,
Christ is risen,
Christ will come again.

B. All: Dying you destroyed our death,
rising you restored our life.
Lord Jesus, come in glory.

C. All: When we eat this bread
and drink this cup,
we proclaim your death, Lord Jesus,
until you come in glory.

D. All: Lord, by your cross and resurrection
you have set us free.
You are the Savior of the world.

Great Amen

Celebrant: *Through him, with him, in him,*
in the unity of the Holy Spirit,
all glory and honor is yours,
almighty Father,
for ever and ever.
All: Amen.

Communion Rite

The Lord's Prayer

All: Our Father, who art in heaven,
hallowed be thy name;
thy kingdom come,

8

thy will be done
on earth as it is in heaven.
Give us this day our daily bread;
and forgive us our trespasses
as we forgive those
who trespass against us;
and lead us not into temptation,
but deliver us from evil.

(short prayer for protection by the Celebrant)

For the kingdom, the power, and the glory
are yours,
now and for ever. Amen.

Sign of Peace

Celebrant: *Lord Jesus Christ,*
you said to your apostles:
I leave you peace,
my peace I give you.
Look not on our sins,
but on the faith of your Church,
and grant us the peace
and unity of your kingdom
where you live for ever and ever.
All: Amen.

Celebrant: *The peace of the Lord*
be with you always.
All: And also with you.

Breaking of the Bread

All: Lamb of God,
you take away the sins of the world:
have mercy on us.
Lamb of God,
you take away the sins of the world:
have mercy on us.
Lamb of God,

you take away the sins of the world:
grant us peace.

Communion

Celebrant: *This is the Lamb of God*
who takes away
the sins of the world.
Happy are those who are called
to his supper.

All: Lord, I am not worthy
to receive you,
but only say the word
and I shall be healed.

Communion Song
Period of Silence or Song of Praise
Prayer After Communion

All: Amen.

Concluding Rite

Greeting

Celebrant: *The Lord be with you.*
All: And also with you.

Blessing

All: Amen.

Dismissal

Celebrant: *Go in the peace of Christ. (or)*
The Mass is ended, go in peace. (or)
Go in peace to love and serve the Lord.

All: Thanks be to God.

Recessional

Rite of Baptism of Children

Introductory Rites
Reception of the Candidates

Liturgy of the Word
Procession
Song
Scripture Readings
General Intercessions
Litany of the Saints

Liturgy of the Sacrament
Prayer of Exorcism

(In this prayer, the Celebrant prays that God will free the candidates from original sin and make them temples of his glory.)

All: Amen.

Anointing Before Baptism

Celebrant: We anoint you with the oil of salvation in the name of Christ, our Savior, may

11

he strengthen you with his power, who
lives and reigns forever and ever.

All: Amen.

Celebration of Baptism

Procession to the Font

(As the procession to the font begins, an appropriate hymn or psalm may be sung.)

Blessing and Invocation of God over Baptismal Water

(The Celebrant blesses the water to be used in Baptism. All respond to the prayer of blessing as instructed.)

Renunciation of Sin and Profession of Faith

(The Celebrant asks the parents and godparents a series of questions to which they respond: I do.)

This section of the rite is concluded with the following community's assent to the Profession of Faith:

Celebrant: *This is our faith. This is the faith of the Church. We are proud to profess it, in Christ Jesus our Lord.*

All: Amen.

Baptism

Celebrant: *Is it your will that N. should be baptized. in the faith of the Church. which we have all professed with you?*

Parents &
Godparents: *It is.*

12

Celebrant:	N., I baptize you in the name of the Father, and of the Son, and of the Holy Spirit.
All:	(respond with appropriate short acclamation)

Anointing with Chrism

Celebrant:	(short prayer of anointing)
All:	Amen.

Clothing with White Garment

Celebrant:	(prayer about the garment and what it symbolizes)
All:	Amen.

Lighted Candle

Celebrant:	Receive the light of Christ.....
	(While the candles are being lit, an appropriate song may be sung.)

Prayer Over the Ears and Mouth

Celebrant:	(short prayer that each may soon hear and proclaim God's word)
All:	Amen.

(After the celebration of Baptism, Mass continues in the usual way, except for the omission of the Creed. If the rite is celebrated outside of Mass, it is concluded as follows: there is a procession to the altar during which an appropriate song may be sung. The Celebrant invites all to sing or proclaim The Lord's Prayer. This is followed by a blessing of the mother, father and all gathered, and may be concluded with a hymn which suitably expresses thanksgiving and Easter joy.)

Rite of Marriage
Within Mass

Introductory Rites

Entrance Procession

(After the procession, the Mass continues as usual with the Liturgy of the Word.)

Liturgy of the Sacrament

The rite begins after the Homily and is celebrated in the following order:
Introduction
Declaration of Intention
Consent
Blessing and Exchange of Rings

The rite is concluded with the General Intercessions, or if the rubrics call for it, the Profession of Faith is said after the General Intercessions.

Liturgy of the Eucharist

The Mass continues as usual.

Nuptial Blessing

The Nuptial Blessing immediately follows The Lord's Prayer.

Solemn Blessing

At the end of Mass, a solemn blessing is given to the couple, and all respond with Amen after each invocation. Then all are blessed, and respond with Amen.

Recessional

Rite of Marriage
Outside of Mass

Introductory Rites

Entrance Procession
Greeting
Opening Prayer

> All: Amen.

Liturgy of the Word

Liturgy of the Sacrament

The rite is celebrated in the following order:

Introduction
Declaration of Intention
Consent
Blessing and Exchange of Rings

The Liturgy of the Sacrament concludes with the Nuptial Blessing.

Concluding Rites

The Lord's Prayer
Blessing
Recessional

Rite of Funerals

Gathering at the Church Entrance

> *Celebrant:*   *(greets the mourners and sprinkles the casket with holy water)*

(The Paschal Candle leads the entrance procession into the church.)

Entrance Song

(In the Funeral Rite, the Penitential Rite is omitted and the Mass continues with the Opening Prayer and follows the usual order. Following the prayer after Communion or, if Mass is not celebrated, following the Liturgy of the Word, the Rite of Final Commendation and Farewell takes place.)

Final Commendation and Farewell

> *Celebrant:*   *(brief introduction and invitation for silent prayer)*

Responsory

(As a suitable song is sung, the Celebrant may sprinkle the casket with holy water and incense it.)

Concluding Prayer

> *Celebrant:*   *....through Christ our Lord.*
>
> All: Amen.

Recessional Song

Songs for Celebration

1   Abba! Father!

Refrain: Jer. 18: 6, Rom. 8: 15
Verse 1: Rom. 8: 29
Verse 2: John 17: 21

REV. CAREY LANDRY

slowly, reverently

Refrain: Ab - ba, _____
1. Mold us, _____
2. Fath - er, _____

Ref. Ab - ba, Fath - er. _____
1. mold us and fash - ion us _____
2. may we be one in You. _____

Ref. You are the pot - ter; _____ of
1. in - to the im - age _____ as
2. May we be one in You _____

Ref. we are the clay, _____ the
1. Je - sus Your son, _____ of
2. He is in You _____ and

Ref. work of Your hands. _____ *(to V. 1, to V. 2, to V. 3)*
1. Je - sus, Your son. _____ *(Refrain)*
2. You are in Him. _____ *(Refrain)*

3. Glo - ry, _____
Last Ref. Ab - ba, _____

Copyright ©1977 by North American Liturgy Resources, 10802 N. 23rd Avenue, Phoenix, Arizona, 85029.
All Rights Reserved.

3. glo - ry and praise to You____
Last Ref. Ab - ba, Fath - er.____

3. Glo - ry and praise to You____ for -
Last Ref. You are the pot - ter;____

3. ev - er, a - men,____ for
Last Ref. we are the clay,____ the

3. ev - er, a - men.____ *(Last Refrain)*
Last Ref. work of Your hands____

Last Ref.____ Ab ba!

All My Days

2

Based on Psalm 8

Music: **DAN SCHUTTE, S.J.**
Lyrics: **JIM MURRAY, S.J.**

Ant: Till the end of my days, O____ Lord,

I will bless your name,____ sing your praise,____

Copyright © 1971 by Daniel L. Schutte, S.J. and James G. Murray, S.J. Published exclusively by North American Liturgy Resources, 10802 N. 23rd Avenue, Phoenix, Arizona 85029. All Rights Reserved.

give you thanks, _____ all my days. _____

1. You have made me lit - tle less than a
3. ( ) Your sun _____ and your moon give me

1. God, _____ and have lav - ished my heart with your love. _____
3. light, _____ and your stars show the way through the night. _____

1. _____ With dig - ni - ty and ho - nor you've clothed me, _____
3. _____ Your ri - vers and streams have re - freshed me. _____

1. _____ giv - en me rule o - ver all. _____
3. _____ I _____ will sing your _____ praise. _____

2. You have blessed me with good things and
4. ( ) How great is your love, O _____

2. plen - ty _____ and sur - round - ed my ta - ble with friends. _____
4. Fa - ther, _____ that you sent us your Sa - vior Son. _____

2. _____ Their love and their laugh - ter en - rich me; _____
4. _____ His death and his ris - ing will heal us, _____

2. _____ to - geth - er we sing your _____ praise. _____
4. _____ and draw us _____ all un - to you. _____

20

Amazing Grace

3

John Newton
1725-1807

Early American Tune
Arranged by HENRY PAPALE

Very Slow (♩ = 48)

1. A - maz - ing grace! How sweet the
2. Through man - y dan - gers, toils and
3. When we've been there ten thou - sand

sound, that saved a wretch like me! I
snares, I have al - read - y come; 'tis
years, bright shin - ing as the sun; we've

once was lost but now am
grace hath brought me safe thus
no less days to sing God's

found, was blind, but now I see.
far, and grace will lead me home.
praise than when we first be - gun.

This arrangement Copyright ©1983 by North American Liturgy Resources,
10802 N. 23rd Ave., Phoenix, Arizona 85029. All rights reserved.

4   And the Father Will Dance

Zephaniah 3: 14 - 17, 19 - 20

REV. CAREY LANDRY

"Shout for joy, daughter of Zion
Rejoice, exult with all your heart
Yahweh your God is in your midst
He will exult with joy over you
He will renew you by his love
He will dance with shouts of joy for you
as on a day of festival"

Vigorously
REFRAIN

And the Fath-er will dance as on a day of joy._

_ He will ex - ult o - ver you_ and re -

1. 3. 5. 7. | 2. 4. 6.

new you by_ His love. love. *(to Verses)*

8.

love. He will re - new you by His love!_ *fine*

VERSES

1. Shout for joy, all you, His peo - ple.

1. Sing a - loud and ex - ult with all your

1. heart, for_ Yah- weh, your God is in your midst. *(Refrain)*

2. You have no more e - vil to fear. You have

Copyright ©1977 by North American Liturgy Resources, 10802 N. 23rd Avenue, Phoenix, Arizona 85029.
All Rights Reserved.

2. no more e - vil to fear. Do not let your hands_ fall

2. limp, for___ Yah-weh, your God is in your midst. *(Refrain)*

3. And when the time comes I will res - cue the

3. lame, and when the time comes I will gath - er the

3. strays, and when the time comes I will be_ your

3. guide. I will gath-er you in___ and

3. give you re - nown a - mong all peo - ples. *(Refrain)*

Are Not Our Hearts   5

Based on Luke 24:13-35

Words and Music by
REV. CAREY LANDRY

Are not our hearts burn - ing with - in us. Are not our

hearts light - ed with fire. Je - sus is with us, is ri - sen is

Copyright © 1973 by Rev. Carey Landry and North American Liturgy Resources, 10802 N. 23rd Avenue, Phoenix, Arizona, 85029. All Rights Reserved. International Copyright secured.

with us. Je - sus is ri - sen, is with us to day.

Je - sus is the Lord! Je -

sus is the Lord.

6. Arise, Come Sing in the Morning

Words and Music
JOE ZSIGRAY

REFRAIN

A - rise, come sing in the morn - ing.

Praise the Lord ev - 'ry day.

Live his love ev - 'ry mo - ment of our

lives; say yes in ev - 'ry

way, ev - 'ry day.

VERSES

1. In the morning the sun will arise
   and shed its warmth upon the earth.
   It is the beginning of a brighter day,
   a time for our rebirth.

2. Through the life of Jesus the Son
   we learn to live, grow and love;
   to see the goodness in each and every day
   that comes from God above.

Copyright ©1973 by North American Liturgy Resources, 10802 N. 23rd Avenue, Phoenix, Arizona, 85029.
All Rights Reserved.

Baptism Prayer

Words and Music by TIM SCHOENBACHLER

REFRAIN

Lord, bless__ this child. Lord, bless__ this child,_____ and keep_____ him__ in the hol-low of your hand,_____ and make the wind__ blow on-ly__ at his back._____ O__ Lord, bless this child.

VERSES

1. Give to him a mo-ther's love, (Ma-ry_____),
2. Give to him a world of joy, (Ma-ry_____),

1. and give to him a Fa-ther's strength, (Fran_____).
2. and give to him a world of hope, (Fran_____).

1. May (Mar-tin) know_____ the love you__ share.
2. May (Mar-tin) know_____ a world of__ peace.

1. May your love bless this child. *(Refrain)*
2. May your love bless this child. *(Refrain)*

Copyright ©1975 by North American Liturgy Resources, 10802 N. 23rd Avenue, Phoenix, Arizona, 85029. All Rights Reserved.

8   Be Not Afraid

Based on Isaiah 43:2-3
and Luke 6:20ff.

BOB DUFFORD, S.J.

1. You shall
1. cross the bar-ren des-ert,_____ but you shall not die of
1. thirst._____ You shall wan-der far in saf-ety_____ though you
1. do not know the way. You shall speak your words in
1. for - eign lands and all will un - der - stand.
cresc.
1. You shall see the face of God and live. _____ *(Antiphon)*
rit.

ANTIPHON

a tempo
Be not_____ a - fraid. I go be -
f
fore you al - ways. Come__ fol-low Me, _____ and
cresc.
I will give you rest._____

Copyright © 1975 by Robert J. Dufford, S.J., and North American Liturgy Resources, 10802 N. 23rd
Avenue, Phoenix, Arizona, 85029. All Rights Reserved.

2. If you pass through rag-ing wa-ters in the sea, ____ you shall not

2. drown. ____ If you walk a-mid the burn-ing flames,

2. you shall not be harmed. If you stand be-fore the

2. pow'r of hell and death is at your

ff   *rit.*

2. side, know that I am with you ____ through it all. ____ (Antiphon)

mf

3. Bless - ed are your poor, ____ for the king - dom shall be

3. theirs. Blest are you that weep and mourn, for

3. one day you shall laugh. And if wick-ed men in-

3. sult and hate you all be-cause of Me,

ff   *rit.*

3. bless-ed, ____ bless-ed ____ are you! ____ (Antiphon)

9 Blessed Be God Forever

ERICH SYLVESTER

1. When the new moon hides and there's some-one dy - ing;
2. When an old man feels that he's been for- sak - en;
3. When a fath - er feels that he'll nev - er make it;
4. When a bab - y longs for the love of moth - er;

Bless-ed be God for - ev - er!

1. Hear the
2. There's a
3. There's a
4. He re-

1. lone - ly sound of the wil - low sigh - ing;
2. new man need - ing to be a - wak - ened;
3. help - ing hand if he'll on - ly take it;
4. veals the love of the one a - bove her;

Bless-ed be God for - ev - er!

Copyright © 1972 by North American Liturgy Resources, 10802 N. 23rd Avenue, Phoenix, Arizona, 85029.
All Rights Reserved.

REFRAIN

When-ev - er we're to - geth - er in warm or storm - y weath - er; oh we can't go wrong if we sing our song; bless-ed be God for - ev - er. - er.

(Refrain may be sung twice after fourth verse if so desired.)

Blest Be the Lord

Based on Psalm 91

DAN SCHUTTE, S.J.

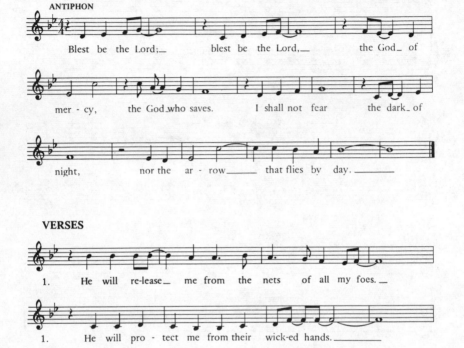

ANTIPHON

Blest be the Lord;__ blest be the Lord,__ the God__ of mer - cy, the God who saves. I shall not fear the dark__ of night, nor the ar - row____ that flies by day. _____

VERSES

1. He will re-lease__ me from the nets of all my foes. __

1. He will pro - tect me from their wick-ed hands._____

1. Be-neath the sha-dow__ of His wings__ I will re - joice__

1. to find a dwell-ing___ place se - cure.___ *(Antiphon)*

2. I need not shrink before the terrors of the night,
    Nor stand alone before the light of day.
    No harm shall come to me, no arrow strike me down,
    No evil settle in my soul.

3. Although a thousand strong have fallen at my side,
    I'll not be shaken with the Lord at hand.
    His faithful love is all the armor that I need
    To wage my battle with the foe.

Copyright ©1976 by Daniel L. Schutte, S.J., and North American Liturgy Resources, 10802 N. 23rd Avenue, Phoenix, Arizona, 85029. All Rights Reserved.

Based on John 4:35-38; Matthew 9:38

DAN SCHUTTE, S.J.

Moderate tempo ♩ = 88

1. The fields are high___ and sum-mer's days are few; green fields have
2. The seeds were sown___ by o-ther hands than yours; nur-tured and

1. turned___ to gold._____ The time is here for the
2. cared for they grew._____ But those who have sown will not

1. har-vest-ing,_____ for ga-ther-ing home in-to barns._____
2. har-vest them;_____ the reap-ing will not be their care._____

CHORUS

The har-vest is plen-ty; la-bor-ers are few. Come with me in-to the

fields._____ Your arms may grow wea-ry; your shoes will wear thin.

1.   2.

Come with me in-to the fields.____ fields.___ Come with me in-to the fields.

Copyright ©1971 by Daniel L. Schutte, S.J. Published exclusively by North American Liturgy Resources, 10802 N. 23rd Avenue, Phoenix, Arizona, 85029. All Rights Reserved.

12 Dwelling Place

Based on Eph. 3: 14-17, 1:2

JOHN FOLEY, S.J.

VERSES

1. I fall on my knees_____ to the Fa -
2. May He in His love_____ give us strength
4. I fall on my knees_____ to the Fa -

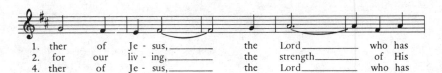

1. ther of Je - sus,_____ the Lord_____ who has
2. for our liv - ing,_____ the strength_____ of His
4. ther of Je - sus,_____ the Lord_____ who has

1. shown us_____ the glo - ry of God._____ *(to v. 2)*
2. Spir - it,_____ the glo - ry of God._____ *(Antiphon)*
4. shown us_____ the glo - ry of God._____ *(Antiphon)*

ANTIPHON

May Christ find a dwell - ing place of faith

in our hearts. May our lives be root - ed in

love, _____ root - ed in love. _____

Copyright ©1976 by John B. Foley, S.J., and North American Liturgy Resources, 10802 N. 23rd Avenue, Phoenix, Arizona, 85029. All Rights Reserved.

3. May grace and peace _____ be yours _____

3. ___ in God _____ our Fa - ther, _____ and

3. in _____ His Son. _____ (Antiphon)

Earthen Vessels   13

Based on 2 Cor. 4:6-7, 1 Cor. 1:27-29   JOHN FOLEY, S.J.

ANTIPHON

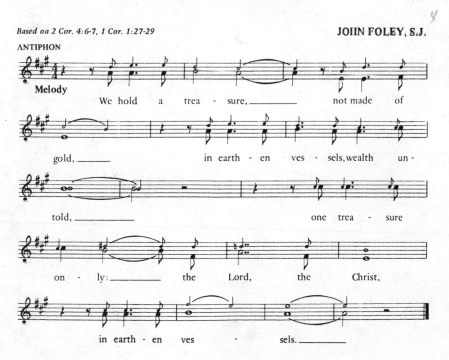

Melody

We hold a trea - sure, _____ not made of

gold, _____ in earth - en ves - sels, wealth un -

told, _____ one trea - sure

on - ly: _____ the Lord, the Christ,

in earth - en ves - sels. _____

Copyright ©1975 by John B. Foley, S.J., and North American Liturgy Resources, 10802 N. 23rd Avenue, Phoenix, Arizona, 85029. All Rights Reserved.

VERSES

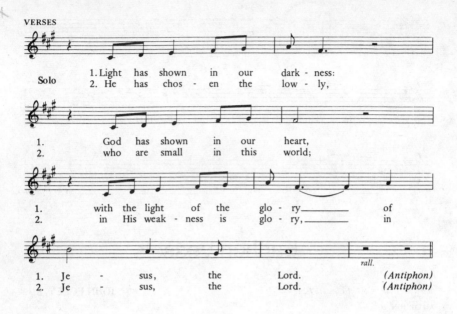

Solo

1. Light has shown in our dark - ness:
2. He has chos - en the low - ly,

1. God has shown in our heart,
2. who are small in this world;

1. with the light of the glo - ry_____ of
2. in His weak - ness is glo - ry,_____ in

rall.

1. Je - sus, the Lord. *(Antiphon)*
2. Je - sus, the Lord. *(Antiphon)*

14. Every Valley

Based on Isaiah 40   **BOB DUFFORD, S.J.**

Lightly ♩ = 104

Ant: Ev - 'ry____ val - ley shall be ex - al - ted and

ev - 'ry hill made low. And all God's_ peo - ple shall

see to - geth - er the glo - ry of the Lord._____

Copyright©1970 by Robert J. Dufford, S.J. Published exclusively by North American Liturgy Resources, 10802 N. 23rd Avenue, Phoenix, Arizona, 85029. All Rights Reserved.

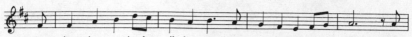

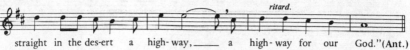

1. A voice cries out in the wil-der-ness: "Pre - pare the way of the Lord. Make

straight in the des-ert a high-way,____ a high-way for our God."(Ant.)

slightly slower

2. Com-fort all my peo - ple; the time for war is gone. The

blind shall see; the deaf shall hear; the lame shall leap for joy. (**Ant.**)

3. Stand up - on the moun-tain top; lift up your voice to the world. Sing

joy - ful- ly Je - ru - sa - lem; be - hold, be-hold your God. (Ant.)

15   Everyone Moved By the Spirit

Based on Romans 8: 14

REV. CAREY LANDRY

REFRAIN

Ev - 'ry one moved by the Spir - it ____ is a son and daugh-ter of God. ____ Led by the fire of His love ____ we will live in the light of the Lord. We will live in the light of the Lord. ____ *Fine*

VERSES

1. Come, O Spir - it of Je - sus. ____
2. Come, O Spir - it of Je - sus. ____

1. Come in the pow - er of His name. ____ Re -
2. Send forth the pow - er of Your love. ____ Re -

1. new ____ the depths ____ of our hearts. ____ *(Refrain)*
2. new ____ the face ____ of the earth. ____ *(Refrain)*

Copyright ©1977 by North American Liturgy Resources, 10802 N. 23rd Avenue, Phoenix, Arizona, 85029.
All Rights Reserved.

16 For You Are My God

Based on Psalm 16

JOHN FOLEY, S.J.

Ant. For You are my God;___ You a-lone are my joy.___ De-fend me, O Lord.___

1. You give mar-ve-lous com-rades to me:___ the faith-ful who dwell in Your land.___ Those who choose a-li-en gods___ have cho-sen an a-li-en band.___ (Antiphon)

2. You are my por-tion and cup;___ it is You that I claim for my prize.___ Your her-i-tage is my de-light,___ the lot you have gi-ven to me.___ (Antiphon)

Copyright©1970 by John B. Foley, S.J. Published exclusively by North American Liturgy Resources, 10802 N. 23rd Avenue, Phoenix, Arizona, 85029. All Rights Reserved.

3. Glad are my heart and my soul; se-cure-ly my bo-dy shall rest. For you will not leave me for dead, nor lead your be-lov-ed a-stray. (Antiphon)

4. You show me the path for my life; in your pre-sence the full-ness of joy. To be at your right hand for-ev-er for me would be hap-pi-ness al-ways. (Antiphon)

Glory and Praise to Our God

Based on Psalms 65 and 66.

DAN SCHUTTE, S.J.

ANTIPHON

Glo - ry and praise to our God, _____ who a - lone gives

light to our days. _____ Man - y are the bless-ings He

bears to those who trust in His ways. _____

VERSES

1. We, the daugh-ters and sons of Him who built the
2. In His wis - dom He strength - ens us, like gold that's
3. Ev - 'ry mom - ent of ev - 'ry day our God is

1. val-leys and plains, _____ praise the won-ders our God has
2. test - ed in fire. _____ Though the pow - er of sin pre -
3. wait-ing to save, _____ al - ways read - y to seek the

cresc.

1. done in ev - 'ry heart that sings. _____ (Antiphon)
2. vails, our God is there to save. _____ (Antiphon)
3. lost, to an - swer those who pray. _____ (Antiphon)

p

4. God has wa - tered our bar - ren land and

f

4. spent His mer - ci - ful rain. _____ Now the

Copyright ©1976 by Daniel L. Schutte, S.J., and North American Liturgy Resources, 10802 N. 23rd Avenue, Phoenix, Arizona, 85029. All Rights Reserved.

Good Morning, Zachary 18

**Words and Music by
ED GUTFREUND**

1. God visits his people and we know him.
His mighty Savior has set us free.

2. The light is before us, leading forward
Awaken the sleeping; we shall be free. *(to Refrain)*

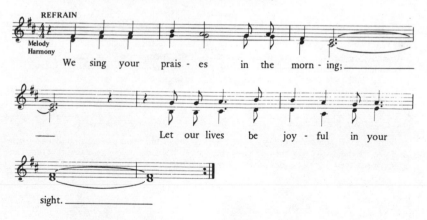

3. You will be a prophet, little child.
Tell all the people they shall be free.

4. A tender companion is our God.
The dawn breaks upon us; we shall be free. *(to Refrain)*

5. Prepare for the Lord, he is coming.
In his forgiveness we shall be free. *(to Verse 2 and Refrain)*

Copyright ©1975 by Ed Gutfreund and North American Liturgy Resources, 10802 N. 23rd Avenue, Phoenix, Arizona, 85029. All Rights Reserved.

19 Great Things Happen When God Mixes With Us!

Words and Music by
REV. CAREY LANDRY

Chorus:

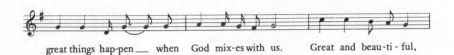

Great things hap-pen___ when God mix-es with us;

great things hap-pen___ when God mix-es with us. Great and beau-ti-ful,

won-der-ful things; Great things hap-pen___ when God mix-es with us.

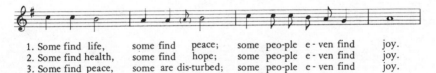

1. Some find life,   some find peace;   some peo-ple e-ven find   joy.
2. Some find health,   some find hope;   some peo-ple e-ven find   joy.
3. Some find peace,   some are dis-turbed; some peo-ple e-ven find   joy.

1. Some see   things as they   nev-er could be-fore and some peo-ple find that they can
2. Some see them-selves as they   nev-er could be-fore and some peo-ple find that they can
3. Some see their lives as they   nev-er could be-fore and some peo-ple find that they must

(CODA)

1. now___   be-gin to   trust.
2. now___   be-gin to   live.   Great things hap-pen___ when
3. now___   be-gin to   change.

God   mix-es with   us.___

Copyright©1971, 1973, and 1977 by Rev. Carey Landry and North American Liturgy Resources, 10802 N. 23rd Avenue, Phoenix, Arizona, 85029. All Rights Reserved. International Copyright secured.

Hail Mary: Gentle Woman 20

Hail Mary based on Luke 1:28

Music and Additional Words by
REV. CAREY LANDRY

Hail Ma - ry,_____ full__ of grace,_____

_ the Lord_____ is with you._____

_ Bless - ed are you a - mong wo - men,_____ and

blest is the fruit of your womb, Je - sus._____

_ Ho - ly Ma - ry,_____

_ Mo - ther of God,_____ pray for us sin - ners

now_____ and at the hour_ of death.

A - men._____ Gen - tle

Copyright ©1975 by Rev. Carey Landry and North American Liturgy Resources, 10802 N. 23rd Avenue, Phoenix, Arizona, 85029. All Rights Reserved.

REFRAIN

wo - man, _____ qui - et light, _____

____ morn - ing star, _____ so strong and bright, _____

____ gen - tle Mo - ther, _____ peace-ful dove, _____

____ teach us wis - dom; _____ teach us love.

VERSE

1. You were chos - en _____ by the

1. Fa - ther; _____ you were chos - en _____

1. ____ for the Son. _____ You were chos - en _____

1. ____ from all wo - men _____ and for

1. wo - man, _____ shin - ing one. _____ Gen-tle
(to Ref.)

2. Bless - ed are you a - mong

2. wo - men._____ Blest in turn_____ all wo - men,

2. too._____ Bless - ed they_____

2. _____ with peace - ful spir - its._____ Bless - ed

2. they_____ with gen - tle hearts._____ Gen - tle

(to Ref.)

How Can I Keep from Singing? 21

TRADITIONAL

**Arrangement by
ED GUTFREUND**

VERSE

1. My life flows on in end - less song a-bove earth's
2. Through all the tu - mult and the strife, I hear the
3. What though the tem - pest 'round me roar, I hear the

1. la - men - ta - tion._____ I hear the real though
2. mu - sic ring - ing._____ It sounds and ech - oes
3. truth, it li - veth;_____ What though the dark - ness

1. far - off hymn that hails a new cre - a - tion._____ *(Ref.)*
2. in my soul; how can I keep from sing-ing?_____ *(Ref.)*
3. 'round me close, songs in the night it gi - veth._____ *(Ref.)*

This arrangement Copyright ©1975 by Ed Gutfreund and North American Liturgy Resources, 10802 N. 23rd Avenue, Phoenix, Arizona, 85029. All Rights Reserved.

REFRAIN

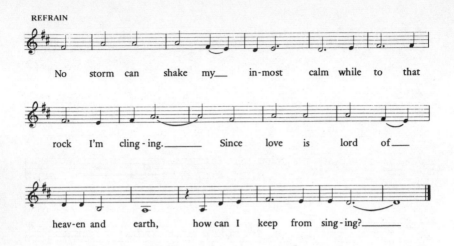

No storm can shake my__ in-most calm while to that

rock I'm cling-ing.____ Since love is lord of__

heav-en and earth, how can I keep from sing-ing?____

22. I Believe in the Sun

*Inspired by an inscription found
in an underground tunnel in
Cologne, Germany after World War II*

**Words and Music by
REV. CAREY LANDRY**

Chorus:

I be - lieve in the sun,____

__ e-ven when it is-n't shin - ing; I be - lieve in love,____

__ e - ven when there's no one there.____ And I be-

lieve in God,____ I be - lieve in God,____ e - ven

Copyright©1973 by Rev. Carey Landry and North American Liturgy Resources, 10802 N. 23rd Avenue,
Phoenix, Arizona, 85029. All Rights Reserved. International Copyright secured.

last time to CODA:

when   He is   si   lent._____

1. I be - lieve_____ in mir - a - cles._____   I be -
2. I be - lieve in the Son of God._____   I be -

1. lieve___ in light._____   I be - lieve   there can al - ways be a
2. lieve___ his way._____   I be - lieve   He can lead us   to the

1. way._____   I   be - lieve that no - thing is   im -
2. light._____   I   be - lieve that He____ is ____

1.   pos - si - ble, I   be - lieve that no-thing is im - pos - si - ble; that
2.   call - ing us, I   be - lieve that He___ is ___   call - ing us; and

1. all   things are   pos - si - ble with   God._____
2. He____   will   lead   us   on   our   way._____

CODA

lent,   e - ven when   He is   si   -   lent.

47

23   I Lift Up My Soul

Based on Psalm 26

TIM MANION

ANTIPHON

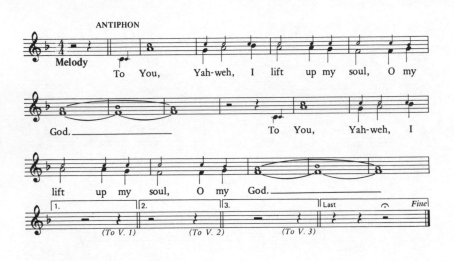

Melody

To You, Yah-weh, I lift up my soul, O my

God._____ To You, Yah-weh, I

lift up my soul, O my God._____

1. (To V. 1)   2. (To V. 2)   3. (To V. 3)   Last   *Fine*

VERSES

1. Yah - weh,_____ show Your ways to me._____

1. Teach me Your paths and keep me in the ways of Your

1. truth,_____ for You are the God that_ saves me._____

1._____   *(Antiphon)*

Copyright ©1976 by Timothy Manion and North American Liturgy Resources, 10802 N. 23rd Avenue, Phoenix, Arizona, 85029. All Rights Reserved.

2. The Lord is so good, so ho - ly,_____

2. sin-ners find the way, and in all that is right He guides the

2. hum - ble._____ The poor He leads in His

2. path - ways._____ *(Antiphon)*

3. All day long I hope in Your good - ness,_____ re -

3. mem - ber Your love, the love that You prom-ised long a -

3. go,_____ and the kind - ness that You gave from of

3. old._____ *(Antiphon)*

49

24   I Will Sing of the Lord

Philippians 2:8, 9, 11 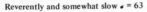   **JOHN FOLEY, S.J.**

Copyright©1972 by John B. Foley, S.J. Published exclusively by North American Liturgy Resources, 10802 N. 23rd Avenue, Phoenix, Arizona, 85029. All Rights Reserved.

If God Is For Us

Based on Romans 8:31-39

JOHN FOLEY, S.J.

Melody

If God is for___ us, who can be a-gainst,___ if the Spir-it of God has set us free.___ If God is for___ us, who can be a-gainst,___ if the Spir-it of God has set us free.___ *Fine*

VERSES

1. I know that no-thing in this world
2. No-thing can take us from His love,
3. And no-thing pre-sent or to come
4. I know that nei-ther death nor life

1. can ev-er take us from His___ love.___ *(Ant.)* If
2. poured out in Je-sus,___ the___ Lord.___ *(Ant.)* If
3. can ev-er take us from His___ love.___ *(Ant.)* If
4. can ev-er take us from His___ love.___ *(Ant.)* If

rall.

Copyright ©1975 by John B. Foley, S.J., and North American Liturgy Resources, 10802 N. 23rd Avenue, Phoenix, Arizona, 85029. All Rights Reserved.

26   If the Lord Does Not Build

Based on Psalm 27 and Jeremiah 9

DAN SCHUTTE, S.J.

ANTIPHON

If the Lord___ does not build a house,___ then in vain___ do the build - ers la - bor.___ And in vain___ does the watch - man stand his guard,___ if the Lord___ is not his___ help,___ if the Lord___ is not his___ help. help.

VERSES

1. If our hearts want to boast,

1. let them boast in the Lord, in the

1. Lord who is kind and___ mer - ci - ful,

Copyright ©1975 by Dan Schutte, S.J., and North American Liturgy Resources, 10802 N. 23rd Avenue, Phoenix, Arizona, 85029. All Rights Reserved.

1. who for-gives our sin. _____ *(Antiphon)*

2. Who are we to com - pare

2. with the Lord who is God?

2. What are we that the Lord should care,

2. or that God should be moved? _____ *(Antiphon)*

3. Trust not in one made of flesh, whose

3. life must fade like the fields. From the

3. earth we are born and to earth re - turn.

3. Let us trust in the Lord. _____ *(Antiphon)*

27   In Him We Live

Rèfrain: Acts: 17: 28
Verse 1: Eph. 1: 4
Verse 2: II Tim. 2: 11

REV. CAREY LANDRY

VERSE - freely; ad lib.

1. Be-fore____ the world was made____ God chose us in

1. Christ   to be His a - dopt - ed ones____ and to

a tempo

1. live   through love   with Him._____

REFRAIN - vigorously; with conviction

In Him   we   live.   In Him   we   move.

In Him   we   are   all that we   are.

In Him   we   live.   In Him   we   move.   In Him   we

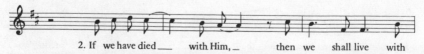

are   all____ that we   are._____   are.

2. If we have died____ with Him,___ then we shall live with

Copyright © 1977 by North American Liturgy Resources, 10802 N. 23rd Avenue, Phoenix, Arizona, 85029.
All Rights Reserved.

2. Him. If we en-dure___ with Him,___ then

2. we shall reign ___ with Him. ___ *(Refrain)*

3. We are His ser - vants,___ the ser - vants of His

3. word. Break-ing the bread of life___ we

3. share___ the bread ___ of His word. ___ *(Refrain)*

In Praise of His Name   28

Based on Ps. 100 and 148

ROC O'CONNOR, S.J.

Bless the Lord, O my soul;___ bless the Lord,

praise His name!___ Bless the Lord, O my soul;___

let all cre - a - tion praise His name!___

Copyright©1976 by Robert F. O'Connor, S.J., and North American Liturgy Resources, 10802 N. 23rd Avenue, Phoenix, Arizona, 85029. All Rights Reserved.

VERSES

1. Sun and the moon, bless the Lord!__ Bless Him, all of the

1. earth! Sea and its waves, glo - ry in your pow'r. Let your

1. thun - der e - cho His name!_____ *(Antiphon)*

2. Let all cre - a - tion a rise and give praise to our

2. God, for Yah-weh a - lone is God. He

2. made us, we be - long to Him!_____ *(Antiphon)*

3. Wom - en and men, praise our God, and

3. child - ren, lift up your hearts. En - ter His gates with

3. songs_ of joy;_ with glad - ness serve you the Lord!_____ *(Antiphon)*

In the Day of the Lord   29

Words and Music by
ED GUTFREUND

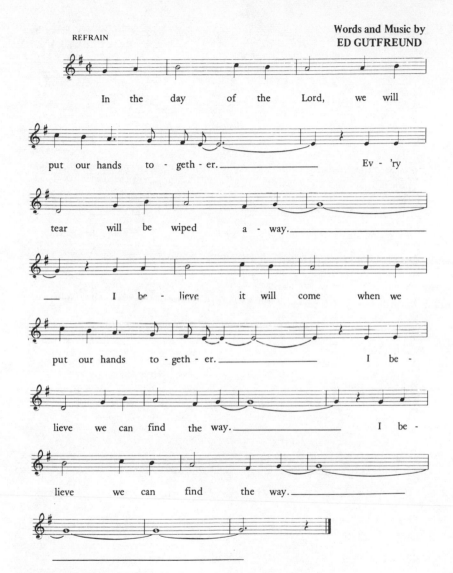

REFRAIN

In the day of the Lord, we will put our hands to-geth-er._____ Ev-'ry tear will be wiped a-way._____ I be-lieve it will come when we put our hands to-geth-er._____ I be-lieve we can find the way._____ I be-lieve we can find the way._____

VERSES

1. Lion and the lamb will lie down,
   swords will plow the earth
   We sit down at the table with our brothers;
   proclaim the Lord here 'til he comes.
   (to Refrain)

2. Father, God of all things living,
   make us as your own.
   Touch our hearts, let us see your light ashining
   as we walk your living land.
   (to Refrain)

Copyright ©1975 by Ed Gutfreund and North American Liturgy Resources, 10802 N. 23rd Avenue, Phoenix, Arizona, 85029. All Rights Reserved.

30   Isaiah 49

Based on Isaiah 49:15

Words and Music by
REV. CAREY LANDRY

1. I will ne - ver for - get you, my

1. peo - ple; I have carved you on the

1. palm___ of my hand. I will

1. ne - ver for - get you; I will

1. not leave you or - phaned. I will

fine

1. ne - ver for - get my own.___

2. Does a mo - ther for - get her

2. ba - by? Or a wo - man___ the

2. child with - in her womb? Yet___

Copyright ©1975 by Rev. Carey Landry and North American Liturgy Resources, 10802 N. 23rd Avenue, Phoenix, Arizona, 85029. All Rights Reserved.

2. e - ven if these for - get, yes,

2. e - ven if these for - get, I will

D.C. al fine

2. ne - ver for - get my own._____

Jesus Is Life   31

(A Triumphant Psalm of Praise to the Risen Lord)

Based on Psalms 148, 149 and 150   **REV. CAREY LANDRY**

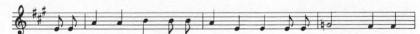

Let the trum - pet blast, let the cym - bals crash, let the danc - ing be -

gin! Let ev - 'ry - thing that breathes pro-claim: Je - sus is

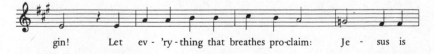

Life! Je - sus is Life!_____

Copyright©1977 by North American Liturgy Resources, 10802 N. 23rd Avenue, Phoenix, Arizona, 85029.
All Rights Reserved.

1. Praise Him with blasts of the trum - pet! Praise Him with lyre and
1. harp! Praise Him with drums and danc - ing!
1. Je - sus is Life! Je - sus is Life!

2. Praise Him with clash - ing cym - bals! Praise Him with strings and
2. reeds! Praise Him with clang - ing cym - bals!
2. Je - sus is Life! Je - sus is Life!

3. Or - chards and for - ests, moun - tains and
3. hills, birds and liv - ing crea - tures
3. dance in praise of His name! _____

4. Praise Him, the Sun of Jus - tice! Praise Him, the King of
4. Kings! Praise Him, our Ris - en Lord!

4. Je - sus is Life! Je - sus is Life!

5. He has been kind to His peo - ple,_____ giv - ing

5. vic - to - ry to us who are weak._____

5. We re - joice and ex - ult in Him!

5. Je - sus our Life!_____

6. Old men and chil - dren too! Young men and

6. girls! Men and wo - men ev - 'ry - where

D. S. al Coda

6. dance in praise of His name!_____

CODA

Ev - er - last - ing Life!_____

61

32 Lay Your Hands

(A Song of Anointing and Forgiveness)

Verse 1: Isaiah 61: 1

REV. CAREY LANDRY

REFRAIN

Lay Your hands gent - ly___ up - on us.___

___ Let their touch ren - der Your peace.___

___ Let them bring Your for - give - ness___ and heal - ing.___

___ Lay Your hands gent - ly, lay Your hands.___

VERSES

1. You were sent___ to free the bro - ken heart - ed. You were

1. sent to give sight to the blind. You de -

1. sire___ to heal all our ill - ness - es. Lay Your

(Refrain)

1. hands gent - ly, lay Your hands.___

Copyright ©1977 by North American Liturgy Resources, 10802 N. 23rd Avenue, Phoenix, Arizona, 85029.
All Rights Reserved.

2. Lord, we come to You through one an - oth - er. _____ Lord, we

2. come to You in our need. Lord, we

2. come to You seek - ing whole - ness. _____ Lay Your

2. hands gent - ly, lay Your hands. *(Last refrain)*

LAST REFRAIN*

Lay Your hands gent - ly _____ up - on us. _____ Let their

touch ren - der Your peace. _____ Let them

bring Your for - give - ness _____ and heal - ing. _____ Lay Your

hands gent - ly, lay Your hands. _____ Lay Your

rit.

hands gent - ly, lay Your hands. _____

33   Let Heaven Rejoice

BOB DUFFORD, S.J.

Ant. Let heaven rejoice and earth be glad: let all creation sing.___ Let children proclaim through ev - 'ry land "Hosanna to our King."

1. Sound the trumpet into the night; the day of the Lord is near.___ Wake His people. lift your voice, proclaim it to the world.___ Let

2. Rise in splendor; shake off your sleep;
Put on your robes of joy.
And in the morning
You shall see the glory of the Lord.

3. Raise your voices, be not afraid.
Proclaim it in ev'ry land:
Christ has died, but he has risen;
He will come again.

4. Sing a new song unto the Lord,
For he has done wonderful deeds.
And praise him, thank him, dance before him,
Play before the Lord.

5. Nations tremble, wise men amazed.
A child is born this night,
Wonderful counsellor, mighty God,
A father, prince of peace.

6. Songs of angels, "Glory on high,
And peace to men on earth.
I bear glad tidings:
Born this day, your savior and your God."

Copyright©1972 by Robert J. Dufford, S.J. Published exclusively by North American Liturgy Resources, 10802 N. 23rd Avenue, Phoenix, Arizona, 85029. All Rights Reserved.

Like a Seal on Your Heart 34

(A Song of Covenant Love)

Based on the Song of Songs 8: 6 - 7, 1: 4

REV. CAREY LANDRY

REFRAIN
Set me like a seal on your heart, like a seal on your arm. Set me like a seal on your heart. How right it is to love you.

VERSES
1. For love is stronger than death, stronger even than hell. The flash of it is a flash of fire, a flame of Yahweh Himself. *(Refrain)*

2. Come, then, my love; come, my beloved. No flood can quench our love, for love, if real, has no end. *(Refrain)*

Copyright ©1977 by North American Liturgy Resources, 10802 N. 23rd Avenue, Phoenix, Arizona, 85029.
All Rights Reserved.

35 Like a Shepherd

Based on Is. 40:9ff; Ez. 34:11ff; Mt. 11:28ff.

BOB DUFFORD, S.J.

ANTIPHON

Like a shep-herd He feeds His flock and gath-ers the
lambs in His arms, _____ hold-ing them care-ful-ly

1-3

close to His heart, _____ lead-ing them home. _____

Last

rit. *Fine*

home, _____ lead-ing them home. _____

VERSES

1. Say to the cit-ies of Ju - dah: _____ Pre - pare __ the
2. I __ my - self __ will shep-herd them, _____ for oth-ers have

1. way of the Lord. _____ Go to the moun-tain top, lift your
2. led them a - stray. _____ The lost I will res - cue and heal their

1. voice: Je - ru - sa-lem, here is your God. _____ *(Antiphon)*
2. wounds and pas - ture them, giv - ing them rest. _____ *(Antiphon)*

3. Come _____ un - to Me _____ if you are

Copyright ©1976 by Robert J. Dufford, S.J., and North American Liturgy Resources, 10802 N. 23rd Avenue, Phoenix, Arizona, 85029. All Rights Reserved.

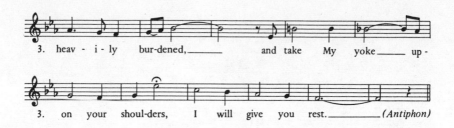

3. heav - i - ly bur-dened,_____ and take My yoke____ up-

3. on your shoul-ders, I will give you rest._____ *(Antiphon)*

Litany 36

**Words and Music by
REV. CAREY LANDRY**

REFRAIN

O Lord, our God, we lift up our hearts to you; O

Lord, our God, your peo-ple re-joice in you.

VERSES

1. Stone of the sa - ges, Cov - e - nant ma - ker,

Fa - ther of mer - cy, we lift up our hearts to you.

2. God of the liv - ing — God of all peo - ple,

Father of life — we lift up our hearts to you.

Copyright©1969 by Rev. Carey Landry and North American Liturgy Resources, 10802 N. 23rd Avenue, Phoenix, Arizona, 85029. All Rights Reserved.

37
Lord of Glory

Based on The Song of Songs

TIM MANION

Briskly; Bluegrass feeling ♩ = 112

ANTIPHON

Melody

Leap-ing the moun-tains, bound-ing the hills,____ see how our God has come to meet us. His voice is lift-ed; His face is joy. Now is the sea-son to sing our song on high.____

1. ____ (to V. 1) ____ 2. (to V. 2) ____ 3. (to V. 3) ____ Last *Fine*

VERSES

1. Come, then, O Lord of glo-ry, show 1. us Your face.____ Speak, for we

Copyright ©1976 by Timothy Manion and North American Liturgy Resources, 10802 N. 23rd Avenue, Phoenix, Arizona, 85029. All Rights Reserved.

1.know Your words are life. _____ *(Antiphon)*

2. He pas - tures His flock a - mong the wild____

2. ____ flow'rs____ and leads them to the

2.moun - tain of His love. _____ *(Antiphon)*

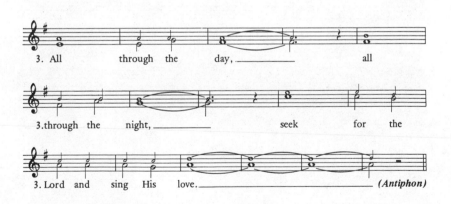

3. All through the day, ____ all

3.through the night, ____ seek for the

3. Lord and sing His love. _____ *(Antiphon)*

69

38
Only a Shadow

Words and Music by
REV. CAREY LANDRY

1. The love_____ I have for you, my Lord,____ is
2. My own_____ be-lief in you, my Lord,____ is

1. on - ly a sha-dow of your love for me;
2. on - ly a sha-dow of your faith in me;

1. on - ly a sha-dow of your love for me, Your
2. on - ly a sha-dow of your faith in me, Your

1. deep_____ a - bid - ing love._____
2. deep_____ and last - ing faith._____

3. My life_____ is in your hands,_____ my

life_____ is in your hands._____ My

love_____ for you will grow, my God; Your

light_____ in me will shine._____

4. The dream I have today, my Lord,
is only a shadow of your dreams for me,
Only a shadow of all that will be,
If I but follow you.

5. The joy I feel today, my Lord,
is only a shadow of your joys for me,
Only a shadow of your joys for me,
When we meet face to face.

vs. 3

Copyright © 1971 by Rev. Carey Landry and North American Liturgy Resources, 10802 N. 23rd Avenue,
Phoenix, Arizona, 85029. All Rights Reserved. International Copyright secured.

70

Peace is Flowing Like a River 39

TRADITIONAL

Based on Psalm 107

Words and Music Adapted by
REV. CAREY LANDRY

1. Peace is flow - ing like a ri -
2. His love is flow - ing like a ri -
3. His heal - ing's flow - ing like a ri -
4.   Al - le - lu - ia, al - le - lu -
5. His peace is flow - ing like a ri -

1. ver, flow - ing out of you and me.
2. ver, flow - ing out of you and me.
3. ver, flow - ing out of you and me.
4. ia. Al - le - lu - ia, al - le - lu -
5. ver, flow - ing out of you and me.

1. ___ Flow - ing out in - to the des -
2. ___ Flow - ing out in - to the des -
3. ___ Flow - ing out in - to the des -
4. ia. Al - le - lu - ia, al - le - lu -
5. ___ Flow - ing out in - to the des -

1. ert, set - ting all the cap - tives
2. ert, set - ting all the cap - tives
3. ert, set - ting all the cap - tives
4. ia. Al - le - lu - ia, al - le -
5. ert, set - ting all the cap - tives

1.2.4.5.   *fine*   3.

1. free. ___   3. free. ___   *(to spoken text)*
2. free. ___
4. lu - ia.
5. free. ___

Spoken:
Dear Father, Brother Jesus,
send the power of your healing upon us your people.
Heal our hearts; renew our spirits.
Enkindle within your people the fire of your love.
Send forth your spirit and we will be recreated,
and you shall renew the face of the earth. *(to Verse 4)*

This arrangement Copyright ©1975 by Rev. Carey Landry and North American Liturgy Resources, 10802 N.
23rd Avenue, Phoenix, Arizona, 85029. All Rights Reserved.

Peace Prayer

Based on a prayer of St. Francis of Assisi

JOHN FOLEY, S.J.

Not too fast ♩ = 88

1. Lord, make me a means of Your peace. _____ Where there's
2. Lord, make me a means of Your peace. _____ Where there's
3. Lord, make me a means of Your peace. _____ When there's
4. Lord, grant me to seek and to share: _____ less to
5. Lord, grant me to seek and to share: _____ to re -
6. Lord. grant me to seek and to share: _____ to for -

1. ha - tred grown, let me sow Your love. _____ Where there's
2. doubt and fear, let me sow Your faith. _____ In this
3. sad - ness here, let me sow Your joy. _____ When the
4. be con - soled than to help con - sole, _____ less be
5. ceive love less than to give love free, _____ just to
6. give in Thee, You've for - giv - en me; _____ for to

1. in - jury, Lord, let for - give-ness be my sword.
2. world's des - pair, give me hope in You to share.
3. dark - ness nears, may Your light dis - pel our fears.
4. un - der - stood than to un - der-stand Your good.
5. give in Thee, just re - ceiv-ing from Your tree.
6. die in Thee, is e - ter-nal life to me.

1.—6. Lord, make me a means of Your peace. _____

Copyright©1976 by John B. Foley, S.J., and North American Liturgy Resources, 10802 N. 23rd Avenue, Phoenix, Arizona, 85029. All Rights Reserved.

41 Play Before the Lord

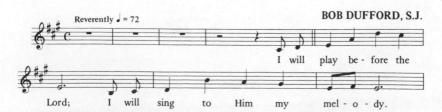

Reverently ♩ = 72

BOB DUFFORD, S.J.

I will play be - fore the Lord; I will sing to Him my mel - o - dy.

Copyright©1972 by Robert J. Dufford, S.J. Published exclusively by North American Liturgy Resources, 10802 N. 23rd Avenue, Phoenix, Arizona, 85029. All Rights Reserved.

Stand a - mong His peo - ple here, tell- ing of all His ways. Let us sing be - fore the Lord; let us sing to Him our mel - o - dy. Stand with - in His tem - ple here, tell- ing of all His ways.

Sing peo - ple of God. Bless His ho - ly name. Of - fer - ing Him our joy - ful hearts, join - ing in end - less praise. Al - le - lu - ia. Al - le - lu - ia. Al - le - lu - ia, le - lu - ia, join - ing in end - less praise.

I will tell- ing of all His ways.

Note: After singing this song through once in its entirety, (i.e. after the first ending), one group of people should go back to the beginning while another group begins at the sign 𝄋 Both parts are sung simultaneously, using chords from the first part.

42   Praise the Lord, My Soul

Based on Psalm 103

JOHN FOLEY, S.J.

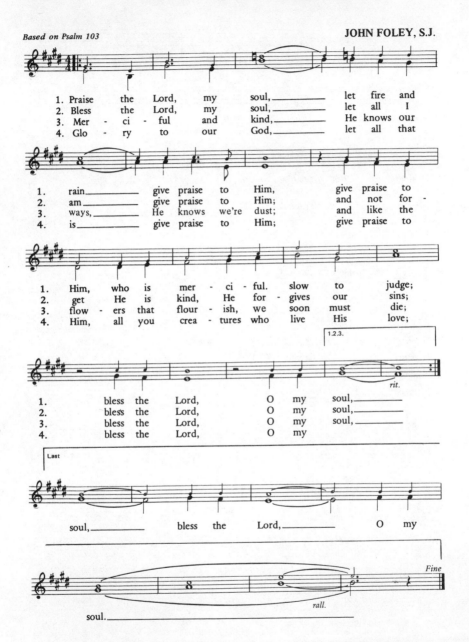

1. Praise the Lord, my soul, ___ let fire and rain ___ give praise to Him, give praise to Him, who is mer-ci-ful, slow to judge; bless the Lord, O my soul, ___
2. Bless the Lord, my soul, ___ let all I am ___ give praise to Him; and not for-get He is kind, He for-gives our sins; bless the Lord, O my soul, ___
3. Mer-ci-ful and kind, ___ He knows our ways, ___ He knows we're dust; and like the flow-ers that flour-ish, we soon must die; bless the Lord, O my soul, ___
4. Glo-ry to our God, ___ let all that is ___ give praise to Him; give praise to Him, all you crea-tures who live His love; bless the Lord, O my

rit.

Last

soul, ___ bless the Lord, ___ O my soul. ___ bless the Lord, ___ O my

rall.   *Fine*

Copyright ©1975 by John B. Foley, S.J., and North American Liturgy Resources, 10802 N. 23rd Avenue, Phoenix, Arizona, 85029. All Rights Reserved.

Psalm 133: Oh, How Good   43

Buoyantly, with spirit

REV. CAREY LANDRY

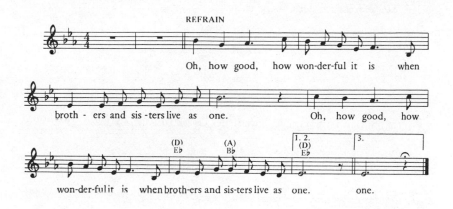

REFRAIN

Oh, how good, how won-der-ful it is when broth - ers and sis -ters live as one. Oh, how good, how won-der-ful it is when broth-ers and sis-ters live as one. one.

(D) Eb (A) Bb 1. 2. (D) Eb 3.

VERSES

1. It is as fra -grant as pure oil, the oint - ment of the Lord, flow - ing down as on Aa - ron of old, a - noint - ing ev - 'ry - one. *(Refrain)*

2. It is as re - fresh - ing as the dew up - on the moun-tain of the Lord, for there the fa - vor of the Lord re-mains, the bless - ing of ev - er - last-ing life. *(Refrain)*

Copyright ©1977 by North American Liturgy Resources, 10802 N. 23rd Avenue, Phoenix, Arizona, 85029. All Rights Reserved.

44   Rise Up, Jerusalem

Based on Isaiah 60:1-4

JOHN FOLEY, S.J.

Reverently and somewhat slowly ♩ = 66

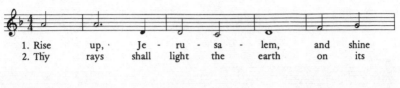

1. Rise up, Je - ru - sa - lem, and shine
2. Thy rays shall light the earth on its

1. forth;_____ thy dawn has come, the glo - ry of the
2. path,_____ and kings shall see the glo - ry of the

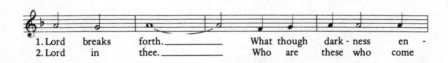

1. Lord breaks forth._____ What though dark - ness en -
2. Lord in thee._____ Who are these who come

1. vel - op the earth,_____ though na - tions with - er in
2. flock - ing to thee?_____ Thy chil - dren, throng - ing to

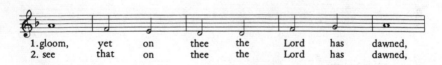

1. gloom, yet on thee the Lord has dawned,
2. see that on thee the Lord has dawned,

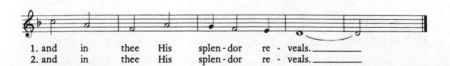

1. and in thee His splen - dor re - veals._____
2. and in thee His splen - dor re - veals._____

Copyright ©1970 by John B. Foley, S.J. Published exclusively by North American Liturgy Resources, 10802 N. 23rd Avenue, Phoenix, Arizona, 85029. All Rights Reserved.

Rise Up, Jerusalem

45

Advent Song

Words and Music by
TIM SCHOENBACHLER

REFRAIN

Rise up, rise up, rise up,— rise up, Je - ru -

- sa - lem!— Sing out, ring out,

sing out,— sing out, Je - ru - sa - lem! Re -

Fine

joice, the day is near!_____

VERSES

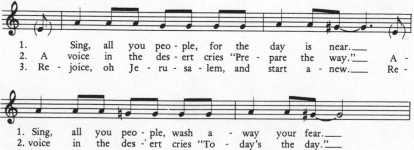

1.   Sing, all you peo - ple, for the day is near.—
2. A voice in the des - ert cries "Pre - pare the way."— A -
3. Re - joice, oh Je - ru - sa - lem, and start a - new.— Re -

1. Sing, all you peo - ple, wash a - way your fear.—
2. voice in the des -'ert cries "To - day's the day."—
3. joice oh Je - ru -'- sa - lem, he comes to you.—

Copyright ©1975 by North American Liturgy Resources, 10802 N. 23rd Avenue, Phoenix, Arizona, 85029.
All Rights Reserved.

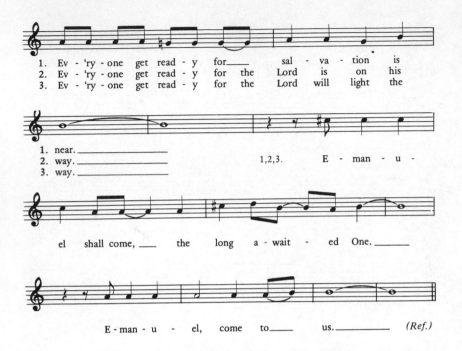

1. Ev - 'ry - one get read - y for____ sal - va - tion is
2. Ev - 'ry - one get read - y for the Lord is on his
3. Ev - 'ry - one get read - y for the Lord will light the

1. near._____
2. way._____   1,2,3.   E - man - u -
3. way._____

el shall come, ___ the long a - wait - ed One. _____

E - man - u - el, come to___ us._____ *(Ref.)*

Seek the Lord

46

Based on Isaiah 55:6-9

ROC O'CONNOR, S.J.

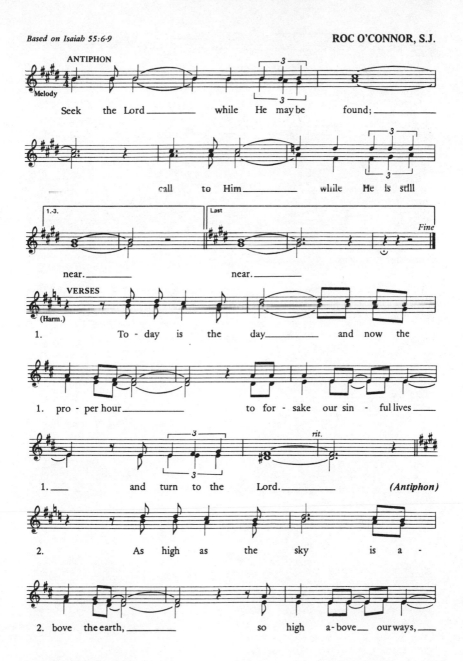

ANTIPHON

Melody

Seek the Lord _____ while He may be found; _____

call to Him _____ while He is still

1.-3.   Last   *Fine*

near. _____   near. _____

VERSES

(Harm.)

1.   To - day is the day _____ and now the

1. pro - per hour _____ to for - sake our sin - ful lives _____

rit.

1. _____ and turn to the Lord. _____ *(Antiphon)*

2.   As high as the sky is a -

2. bove the earth, _____ so high a - bove _____ our ways, _____

Copyright ©1975 by Robert F. O'Connor, S.J., and North American Liturgy Resources, 10802 N. 23rd Avenue, Phoenix, Arizona, 85029. All Rights Reserved.

2. ___ the ways of the Lord.___ *(Antiphon)*

(Harm.)

3. Find - ing the Lord, let us

3. cling to Him.___ His words, His ways ___

3. ___ lead us to life.___ *(Antiphon)*

4. Some - day we'll live in the

4. house of God;___ gaze on His face

4. and praise ___ His name.___ *(Antiphon)*

Sing a New Song

47

Based on Psalm 98

DAN SCHUTTE, S.J.

Joyfully, with spirit ♩ = 132

Ant: Sing a new song un-to the Lord; let your song be
sung from moun-tains high. Sing a new song
un-to the Lord, sing-ing al - le - lu - ia.

1. Yah - weh's peo - ple dance for joy. O come be -
2. Rise, O child - ren, from your sleep; your Sa - vior
3. Glad my soul for I have seen the glo - ry

1. fore the Lord._____ And play for Him on
2. now has come._____ He has turned your
3. of the Lord._____ the trum - pet sounds; the

1. glad tam - bou - rines, and let your trum - pet sound._____ *(Antiphon)*
2. sor - row to joy, and filled your soul with song._____ *(Antiphon)*
3. dead shall be raised. I know my Sa - vior lives. _____ *(Antiphon)*

Copyright ©1972 by Daniel L. Schutte, S.J. Published exclusively by North American Liturgy Resources, 10802 N. 23rd Avenue, Phoenix, Arizona, 85029. All Rights Reserved.

48 Sing to the Mountains

Based on Ps. 118   BOB DUFFORD, S.J.

ANTIPHON

Sing to the moun-tains, sing to the sea. Raise your

voi - ces, lift your hearts. This is the day the

Lord has made. Let all____ the earth re - joice.____

VERSES

1. I will give thanks to You, my Lord. You have

1. an-swered my plea.____ You have saved my soul from

1. death. You are my strength and my song.____ *(Antiphon)*

2. Ho - ly, Ho - ly, Ho - ly

2. Lord.____ Hea - ven and earth are

Copyright ©1975 by Robert J. Dufford, S.J., and North American Liturgy Resources, 10802 N. 23rd Avenue, Phoenix, Arizona, 85029. All Rights Reserved.

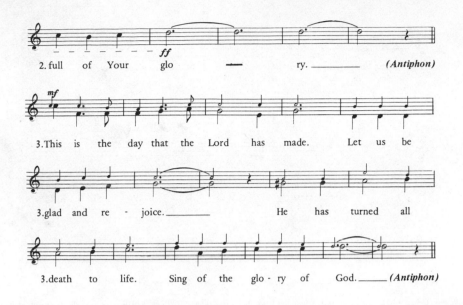

2. full of Your glo — ry. _____ *(Antiphon)*

3. This is the day that the Lord has made. Let us be

3. glad and re - joice. _____ He has turned all

3. death to life. Sing of the glo - ry of God. _____ *(Antiphon)*

A Song for the Masses   49

Words and Music by
TIM SCHOENBACHLER

REFRAIN

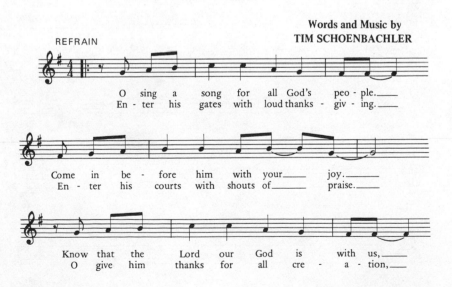

O sing a song for all God's peo - ple.____
En - ter his gates with loud thanks - giv - ing. ____

Come in be - fore him with your____ joy.____
En - ter his courts with shouts of_____ praise.____

Know that the Lord our God is with us,____
O give him thanks for all cre - a - tion,____

Copyright ©1975 by North American Liturgy Resources, 10802 N. 23rd Avenue, Phoenix, Arizona, 85029.
All Rights Reserved.

Song of Baptism 50

Words and Music by
REV. CAREY LANDRY

Chorus:

See this child be - fore you, Lord.

You, who give her life._____ Keep her in Your

sight, O Lord, now and all her days._____

1. She is born, born a - gain, in the sight of us

all._____ With great joy and love for her, joined as

one we pray. _____ 2. Child of love, child of

pain; child of sor - row and joy._____ Child of

two who live as one. Born a - gain to - day._____

Copyright©1969 and 1973 by Rev. Carey Landry and North American Liturgy Resources, 10802 N. 23rd Avenue, Phoenix, Arizona, 85029. All Rights Reserved.

The Spirit is A-Movin' 51

Pentecost 1967

Words and Music by
REV. CAREY LANDRY

Chorus:

The Spir - it is a - mov - in' all

Copyright©1969 by Rev. Carey Landry and North American Liturgy Resources, 10802 N. 23rd Avenue, Phoenix, Arizona, 85029. All Rights Reserved.

o - ver, all o - ver this land. _____

1. Peo - ple are ga - ther - in', the church is born; The

Spir - it is a - blow - in' on a world re - born. _____

2. Doors are opening as the Spirit comes,
   His fire is burning in His people now.

3. Old men are dreaming dreams,
   And young men and women see the light.

4. Old walls are falling down,
   And people all over are speaking with each other.

5. Filled with the Spirit we are sent to serve,
   We are called out as brothers, we are called to work.

6. The Spirit fills us with His power,
   To be His witnesses to all we meet.

7. God has poured out His Spirit,
   On all — on all of mankind.

52   Stay With Me

ERICH SYLVESTER

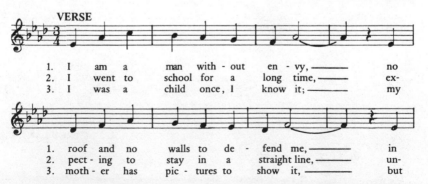

VERSE

1. I am a man with - out en - vy, _____ no
2. I went to school for a long time, _____ ex-
3. I was a child once, I know it; _____ my

1. roof and no walls to de - fend me, _____ in
2. pect - ing to stay in a straight line, _____ un-
3. moth - er has pic - tures to show it, _____ but

Copyright ©1972 By North American Liturgy Resources, 10802 N. 23rd Avenue, Phoenix, Arizona, 85029.
All Rights Reserved.

1. hope that some - day you'll be - friend me,—————— and
2. til I dis - cov -ered that great minds ——— don't
3. she al - ways knew I'd out - grow it; ——— I

1. take all my trou - bles a - way.——————
2. move in a straight line at all. ——————
3. guess that's what pic - tures are for. ——————

REFRAIN

Walk with me, talk with me,

tell me a - bout all the good things you've done;

stay with me, pray with me,

rit.

leave all your blues in your shoes at the

1.
door. *(guitar)* to verse 2. door.

87

53 Take, Lord, Receive

Prayer from Spiritual Exercises, No. 234　　　　　　　　　　　　**JOHN FOLEY, S.J.**

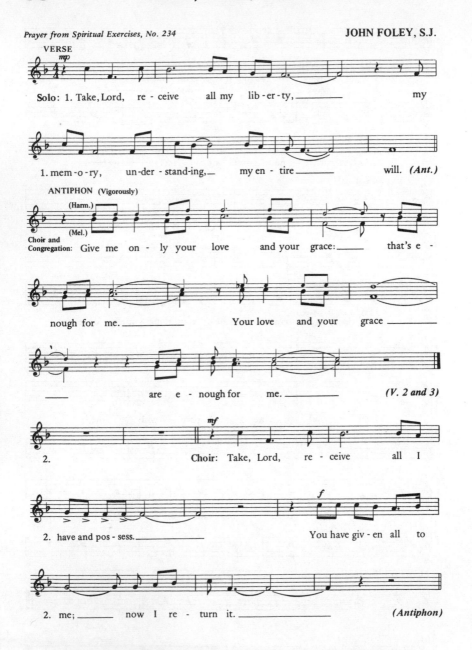

Copyright ©1975 by John B. Foley, S.J., and North American Liturgy Resources, 10802 N. 23rd Avenue, Phoenix, Arizona, 85029. All Rights Reserved.

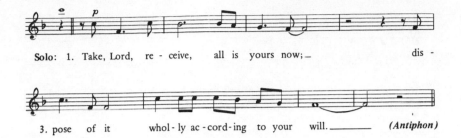

Solo: 1. Take, Lord, re - ceive, all is yours now; _ dis -

3. pose of it whol - ly ac - cord - ing to your will. _____ *(Antiphon)*

This is a Holy Day 54

Words and Music by
ERICH SYLVESTER

1. From the dawn of cre - a - tion when
2. All you bro - thers and sis - ters, put
3. Go and find me a stran - ger who's

1. all things were named, _____ this was a ho - ly
2. down all your bur - dens. _____ This is a ho - ly
3. nev - er been told _____ that this is a ho - ly

1. day. _____ To the day of sal - va -
2. day. _____ We must com - fort the sick, _
3. day. _____ And we'll make him a mem -

1. - tion, _ when death was a - shamed, _____
2. _____ the lone - ly and hurt _____ ones. _____
3. - ber of the heav - en - ly fold. _____

1. this was a ho - ly day. _____
2. This is a ho - ly day. _____
3. This is a ho - ly day. _____

Copyright ©1975 by North American Liturgy Resources, 10802 N. 23rd Avenue, Phoenix, Arizona, 85029.
All Rights Reserved.

REFRAIN:

This is a ho - ly day,_____

_____ this is a ho - ly day.__

_____ I'm gon - na sing,

shout, and write home a - bout_____ it.

This is a ho - ly day._____

55   Though the Mountains May Fall

Based on Isaiah 54:6-10, 49:15,
40:31-32

DAN SCHUTTE, S.J.

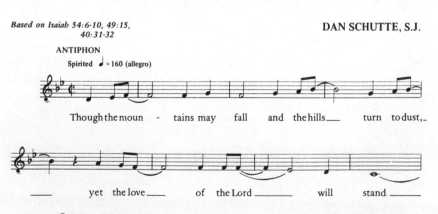

ANTIPHON

Spirited ♩ = 160 (allegro)

Though the moun - tains may fall and the hills__ turn to dust,_

____ yet the love__ of the Lord _____ will stand.____

Copyright ©1975 by Daniel L. Schutte, S.J., and North American Liturgy Resources, 10802 N. 23rd Avenue,
Phoenix, Arizona, 85029. All Rights Reserved.

as a shel - ter for all who will call___ on His name.___

Fine

___ Sing the praise___ and the glo - ry of God._____

VERSES
More Gently

1. Could the Lord ev - er leave you? Could the
2. Should you turn and for - sake Him, He will

1. Lord for - get His love?_____
2. gent - ly call your name._____

1. Though a mo - ther for - sake her child, He will
2. Should you wan - der a - way from Him, He will

crescendo *ff*

1. not a - ban - don you._____ *(Antiphon)*
2. al - ways take you back._____ *(Antiphon)*

3. Go to Him when you're wear - y; He will
4. As He swore to your Fa - thers, when the

3. give you ea - gle's wings._____
4. flood des - troyed the land._____

3. You will run, nev - er tire,_____ for your
4. He will nev - er for - sake you;_____ He will

crescendo *ff*

3. God will be your strength._____ *(Antiphon)*
4. swear to you a - gain._____ *(Antiphon)*

56 A Time for Building Bridges

Words and Music by
REV. CAREY LANDRY

VERSE

1. There's a time for lov - ing___ and a

1. time for em - brac - ing. There's a time for

1. throw - ing___ all past stones a - way. There's a

1. time for heal - ing___ and a time for for -

1. giv - ing.___ There's a time___ for build - ing

1. brid - ges, and that time___ is now.___ Oh,

REFRAIN

take___ our hearts, Lord; take___ our

minds. Take___ our hands, Lord, and

Copyright ©1975 by Rev. Carey Landry and North American Liturgy Resources, 10802 N. 23rd Avenue, Phoenix, Arizona, 85029. All Rights Reserved.

make them one. Take_____ our

hearts, Lord; take_____ our minds.

fine

Take_____ our hands, Lord, and make them one.

VERSE

2. There's a time for re - new ing___ and a

2. time_____ for re - con - cil - ing. There's a

2. time for bind - ing up___ the wounds of the

2. years. There's a time for plant - ing___ and a

2. time for sow - ing.___ There's a time for

2. grow - ing___ the seeds of u - ni - ty. Oh, *(Refrain)*

57

Turn to Me

Based on Isaiah 45:22-23,
51:12,4,6

JOHN FOLEY, S.J.

ANTIPHON

Turn to me, O turn, and be saved, says the Lord, for I am God;___ there is no oth - er, none be - side me.___ I call your name.___

(Verse)

VERSE

a tempo

Solo: 1. I___ am He___ that com-forts you; ___ who are 1. you to be a - fraid ___ of flesh that fades, is

slightly faster

Copyright ©1975 by John B. Foley, S.J., and North American Liturgy Resources, 10802 N. 23rd Avenue, Phoenix, Arizona, 85029. All Rights Reserved.

1. made like the grass of the field soon to with-er.___ *(Antiphon)*

Solo: 2. Lis - ten to me, my peo-ple;___ give ear to

2. me, my na-tion:___ a law will go forth from

2. me, and my jus-tice for a light to the peo-ple.___*(Antiphon)*

Choir: 3. Lift up your eyes to the hea-vens,___ and

3. look at the earth down be - low.___ The

3. hea - vens will va - nish like smoke, and the earth will wear

3. out___ like a gar-ment.___ *(Antiphon)*

95

58   Yahweh, the Faithful One

Based on Genesis 12:1-2; 13:14-17; 15:1-6

DAN SCHUTTE, S.J.

Ant. Yah-weh's love __ will last for - ev - er, ____ his faith - ful-ness till the end of time. ____ Yah - weh is a lov-ing God. ____ Yah - weh, the faith - ful One. ____ *Fine*

1. Have no fear, for I am with you; ____ I ____ will be your shield. ____ Go now and leave your home-land, ____ for I will give you a home. ____ *(Antiphon)*

2. You shall be my cho-sen peo-ple ____ and I will

Copyright ©1970 by Daniel L. Schutte, S.J. Published exclusively by North American Liturgy Resources,
10802 N. 23rd Avenue, Phoenix, Arizona, 85029. All Rights Reserved.

be your God.____ I will bless your name for-

rit.

e-ver____ and keep you from all harm.____(Antiphon)

3. Look up and see the hea-vens____ and count__ the

stars if you can.____ your name will be____ e-ven

rit.

great-er,____ great-er than all these stars.____(Antiphon)

4. See now the land be-fore you,____ rich__ with food and rain.____ No

rit.

long-er____ must you wan-der,____ for this will be your home.(Antiphon)

59 You Are Near

Based on Psalm 139   DAN SCHUTTE, S.J.

Peacefully ♩ = 80

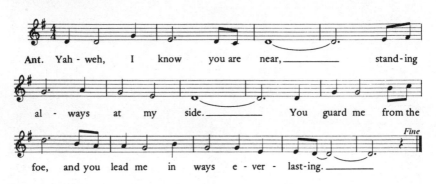

Ant. Yah - weh, I know you are near,_____ stand-ing

al - ways at my side._____ You guard me from the

foe, and you lead me in ways e - ver - last-ing._____

Fine

1. Lord, you have searched my heart, and you

know when I sit and when I stand. Your__ hand is up-on me pro-

slowing   *ritard.*

tect-ing me from death, keep-ing me from harm. _____ (Antiphon)

2. Where can I run from your love?
   If I climb to the heavens you are there;
   If I fly to the sunrise or sail beyond the sea,
   Still I'd find you there.

3. You know my heart and its ways,
   You who formed me before I was born
   In secret of darkness before I saw the sun
   In my mother's womb.

4. Marvelous to me are your works;
   How profound are your thoughts, my Lord.
   Even if I could count them, they number as the stars,
   You would still be there.

Copyright ©1971 by Daniel L. Schutte, S.J. Published exclusively by North American Liturgy Resources,
10802 N. 23rd Avenue, Phoenix, Arizona, 85029. All Rights Reserved.

You Have Been Baptized in Christ 60

From the Rite of Christian Initiation

REV. CAREY LANDRY

VERSES

1. God the Fa-ther has freed you and giv-en you a new

Copyright ©1977 by North American Liturgy Resources, 10802 N. 23rd Avenue, Phoenix, Arizona, 85029.
All Rights Reserved.

birth, and to be a mem - ber of His ho - ly peo - ple He

now an-noints___ you with oil. *(Refrain)*

2. You are a new___ cre - a - tion. In Christ you have___ been

2. clothed. See in this gar - ment the out - ward sign___ of your

2. dig - ni - ty___ in Him. *(Refrain)*

3. Re - ceive the light___ of Christ; keep it burn - ing

3. bright - ly. Al - ways walk___ as a child of the light,___ with His

3. flame a - live___ in your heart. *(Refrain)*

61   Lord, Have Mercy

Music by
ERICH SYLVESTER

Music Copyright ©1972 and 1975 by North American Liturgy Resources, 10802 N. 23rd Avenue, Phoenix, Arizona, 85029. All Rights Reserved.

VERSE

Have mer - cy on us, and for - give us our sins, and

lead us all to ev - er - last - ing life. So I sing

2.
Christ, have__ mer - - cy.__

Lord, have__ mer - cy.__ Lord, have__ mer - cy.__

Lord, have__ mer - - cy.__

Kyrie

JOE ZSIGRAY

Cantor:
Am

Lord, have mer - cy. Lord, have mer - cy.

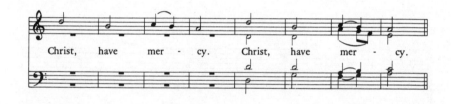

Christ, have mer - cy. Christ, have mer - cy.

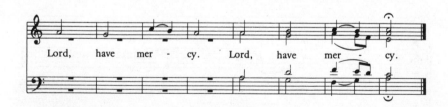

Lord, have mer - cy. Lord, have mer - cy.

Copyright ©1976 by North American Liturgy Resources, 10802 N. 23rd Avenue, Phoenix, Arizona, 85029.
All Rights Reserved.

Gloria

JOE ZSIGRAY

Cantor:

Glo-ry to God__ in the high-est, and peace to His peo - ple on earth.

REFRAIN

S A

Glo - ry to God__ in the high - est, and

T B

peace to His peo - ple on earth. earth. *(to Verse)*

1. 2.

VERSES (Cantor)

1. Lord God, heav-en-ly King,__ al - might-y God and Fa - ther. *(Ref.)*

2. We wor-ship__ You, __ we give__ You thanks,__ we

2. praise You for__ Your great glo - ry. *(Ref.)*

Copyright ©1976 by North American Liturgy Resources, 10802 N. 23rd Avenue, Phoenix, Arizona, 85029.
All Rights Reserved.

3. Lord Je - sus Christ,___ on - ly Son of the Fa -

3. ther, Lord God,___ Lamb___ of God.___ *(Ref.)*

Slower

4. You take a - way the sins of the world; have

4. mer - cy on us. You are seat - ed at the right hand of the

a tempo

4. Fa-ther;___ re - ceive___ our prayer. *(Ref.)*

5. For You a - lone___ are the Ho - ly One;___ You a-lone___ are the Lord.___

5. ___ You a - lone___ are the most high___

5. Je - sus Christ, with the Ho - ly___

5. Spir - it,___ in the Glo - ry of God the___ Fa - ther. *(Ref.)*

S
A

6. A - men, a - men, a - men!

T
B

106

Glory to God

64

Music by
WENDY VICKERS

Glo - ry to God in the high - est, and peace to his peo - ple on earth. Lord___ God, hea - ven - ly King, al - might - y God___ and Fa - - ther, we wor - ship you, we___ give you thanks, we praise you for___ your glo - ry.___ Lord Je - sus Christ, on - ly Son of the Fa - ther, Lord God, Lamb of God,___ you take___ a - way the___

Music Copyright ©1975 by North American Liturgy Resources, 10802 N. 23rd Avenue, Phoenix, Arizona, 85029.

sin of the world: have mer - cy on⎯⎯⎯

us; you are seat - ed at the right

hand of the Fa - ther: re - ceive⎯ our

prayer.⎯⎯⎯ For you⎯ a - lone are the

ho - ly one, you a - lone are the

Lord, you a - lone are⎯ the most

high, Je - sus Christ,⎯⎯⎯ with the

Ho - ly Spir - it, in the

glo - ry of God⎯ the Fa - ther.⎯⎯⎯

A - men, a - men,

a - - - - - men,

a - - - - - - men,

rit.

a - - - men.

Alleluia, Praise to the Lord 65

Words and Music by
ED GUTFREUND

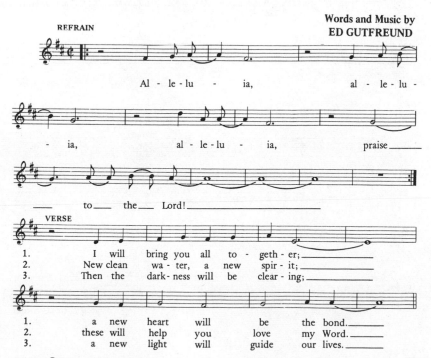

REFRAIN

Al - le - lu - ia, al - le - lu -

- ia, al - le - lu - ia, praise

to the Lord!

VERSE

1. I will bring you all to - geth - er;
2. New clean wa - ter, a new spir - it;
3. Then the dark - ness will be clear - ing;

1. a new heart will be the bond.
2. these will help you love my Word.
3. a new light will guide our lives.

Copyright©1975 by Ed Gutfreund and North American Liturgy Resources, 10802 N. 23rd Avenue, Phoenix, Arizona, 85029. All Rights Reserved.

66 Alleluia

ERICH SYLVESTER

Al - le - lu - ia, al - le - lu - ia,

al - le - lu ia. Al - le - lu - ia,

1.

to verse

al - le - lu - ia, al - le - lu - ia.

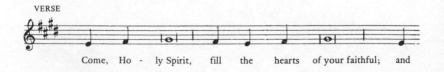

VERSE

Come, Ho - ly Spirit, fill the hearts of your faithful; and

Copyright ©1972 by North American Liturgy Resources, 10802 N. 23rd Avenue, Phoenix, Arizona, 85029.
All Rights Reserved.

kin - dle in them   the   fire of   your   love.   So I sing

al - le - lu - ia, ———   al - le - lu - ia,

al - le - lu - ia,   al - le - lu - ia.———

Holy, Holy

Music by
WENDY VICKERS

Ho - ly, ho - ly, ho - ly Lord, God of pow - er and might. Hea - ven and earth are full of your glo - ry. Ho - san - na in the high - est. Bless - ed is He who comes in the name of the Lord. Ho - san - na in the high - est. Bless - ed is He who comes in the name of the Lord. Ho - san - na in the high - est.

Music Copyright ©1975 by North American Liturgy Resources, 10802 N. 23rd Avenue, Phoenix, Arizona, 85029. All Rights Reserved.

Holy

BOB DUFFORD, S.J.
DAN SCHUTTE, S.J.

Ho - ly, Ho - ly, Ho - ly Lord, God of pow'r and might. Hea - ven and earth are filled with your glo - ry. Ho - san - na, Ho - san - na, on high. Bless - ed is he who comes in the name of the Lord. Ho - san - na in the high - est. Ho - san - na in the high - est. Ho - san - na, ho - san - na on high.

Copyright©1973 by Robert J. Dufford, S.J. and Daniel L. Schutte, S.J. Published exclusively by North American Liturgy Resources, 10802 N. 23rd Avenue, Phoenix, Arizona, 85029. All Rights Reserved.

Anamnesis

JOE ZSIGRAY

Celebrant:

Let us pro-claim _____ the mys-t'ry of our faith: _____

All:

Lord Je-sus, You came ___ and You died _____ for us ___

Lord Je-sus, You rose ___ from the dead. _____

Lord Je-sus, You'll come ___ a-gain in glo ry. ___

___ You'll come a-gain and take Your peo - ple home. ___

_____ You'll come a-gain and

take your peo - ple home. _____

Copyright ©1976 by North American Liturgy Resources, 10802 N. 23rd Avenue, Phoenix, Arizona, 05020.
All Rights Reserved.

Anamnesis 70

Music by
TIM SCHOENBACHLER

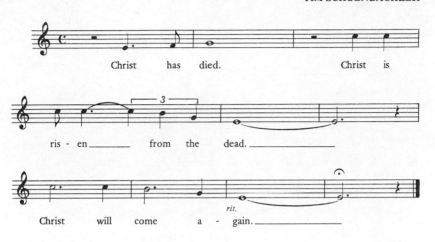

Christ has died. Christ is ris - en from the dead. Christ will come a - gain.

rit.

Music Copyright © 1975 by North American Liturgy Resources, 10802 N. 23rd Avenue, Phoenix, Arizona, 85029. All Rights Reserved.

Dying You Destroyed Our Death 71

ERICH SYLVESTER

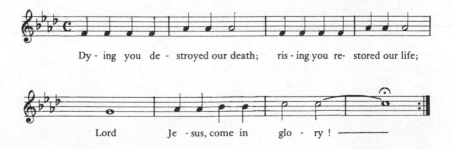

Dy - ing you de - stroyed our death; ris - ing you re - stored our life; Lord Je - sus, come in glo - ry!

Copyright © 1972 by North American Liturgy Resources, 10802 N. 23rd Avenue, Phoenix, Arizona, 85029. All Rights Reserved.

72

Lord, By Your Cross
and Resurrection

Music by
JOE ZSIGRAY

Harmony

Melody

Lord, by Your cross and re - sur - rec - -

tion, ____ You have set ____ us free. ____

____ You are ____ the Sa - vior of the world. ____

1. | 2.

Copyright ©1976 by North American Liturgy Resources, 10802 N. 23rd Avenue, Phoenix, Arizona, 85020.
All Rights Reserved.

When We Eat This Bread   73

REV. CAREY LANDRY

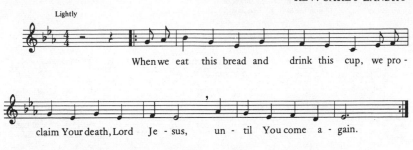

When we eat this bread and drink this cup, we pro-
claim Your death, Lord Je - sus, un - til You come a - gain.

Copyright ©1977 by North American Liturgy Resources, 10802 N. 23rd Avenue, Phoenix, Arizona, 85029.
All Rights Reserved.

When We Gather . . . We Proclaim 74

Based on I Corinthians 11:26

Words and Music by
ED GUTFREUND

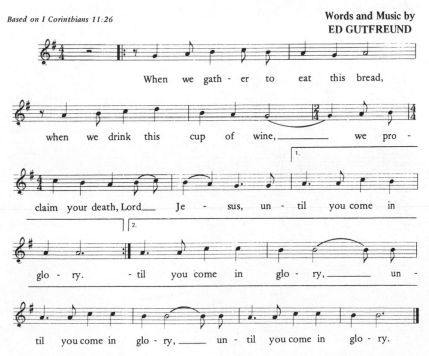

When we gath - er to eat this bread,
when we drink this cup of wine,_____ we pro-
claim your death, Lord___ Je - sus, un - til you come in
1. glo - ry. - til you come in glo - ry,_____ un -
2. til you come in glo - ry,_____ un - til you come in glo - ry.

Copyright ©1975 by Ed Gutfreund and North American Liturgy Resources, 10802 N. 23rd Avenue, Phoenix,
Arizona, 85029. All Rights Reserved.

117

75 Doxology

BOB DUFFORD, S.J.

The first portion may be chanted by the celebrant or
by the entire congregation in the style of free chant:

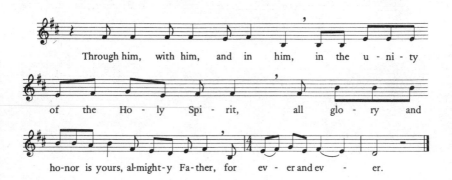

Through him, with him, and in him, in the u-ni-ty
of the Ho-ly Spi-rit, all glo-ry and
ho-nor is yours, al-might-y Fa-ther, for ev-er and ev - er.

Any one of the three "Amen" endings may be used.

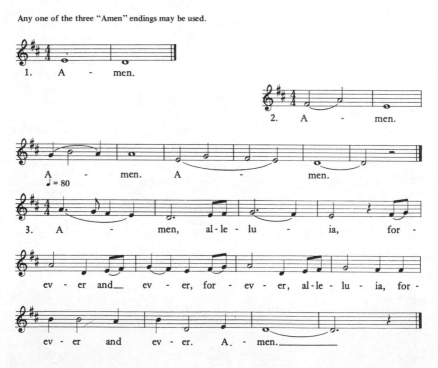

1. A - men.

2. A - men.

A - men. A - men.

♩ = 80

3. A - men, al-le-lu - ia, for-
ev - er and__ ev - er, for - ev - er, al-le-lu - ia, for-
ev - er and ev - er. A. - men.__

Copyright ©1973 by Robert J. Dufford, S.J. Published exclusively by North American Liturgy Resources,
10802 N. 23rd Avenue, Phoenix, Arizona, 85029. All Rights Reserved.

Words and Music by
TIM SCHOENBACHLER

A - men, a - men, a

men, a - men, _____ a - (rit.) - men.

Music Copyright ©1975 by North American Liturgy Resources, 10802 N. 23rd Avenue, Phoenix, Arizona, 85029. All Rights Reserved. English text ©1969 by International Committee on English in the Liturgy, Inc.

Amen 77

ERICH SYLVESTER

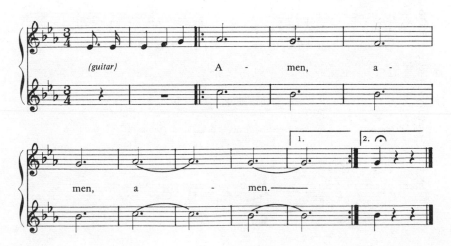

(guitar)   A - men, a -

men, a - men. _____

Copyright ©1972 by North American Liturgy Resources, 10802 N. 23rd Avenue, Phoenix, Arizona, 85029. All Rights Reserved.

78   The Lord's Prayer

ERICH SYLVESTER

Our Fath-er,   who art in heav-en,

hal-low'd be Thy   name;_____   Thy king-dom come;_____

Thy will be done _____   on earth_ as it is_ in

heav-en._   Give us this day our_ dai - ly bread,_ and for-

give us_   our tres-pass-es_   as   we for-give those who tres-pass a

gainst us;_   and lead us not in - to_____ temp-ta - tion,

but de-liv-er   us_____ from e - vil.

Copyright ©1972 by North American Liturgy Resources, 10802 N. 23rd Avenue, Phoenix, Arizona, 85029.
All Rights Reserved.

Spoken by priest or cantor: Deliver us, Lord, from every evil
And grant us peace in our day
In Your mercy keep us free from sin
And protect us from all anxiety
As we wait in joyful hope
For the coming of our Savior, Jesus Christ.

For the king - dom   and the pow - er   and the glo - ry are Yours, ___ now   and for - ev - er, ___ a - men, ___ a - men.

79

Lamb of God

ERICH SYLVESTER

Copyright ©1972 by North American Liturgy Resources, 10802 N. 23rd Avenue, Phoenix, Arizona, 85029.
All Rights Reserved.

Lamb of God, you take a - way the sins of the world: ——— Grant us, grant us peace, grant us peace. ———

Lamb of God

JOE ZSIGRAY

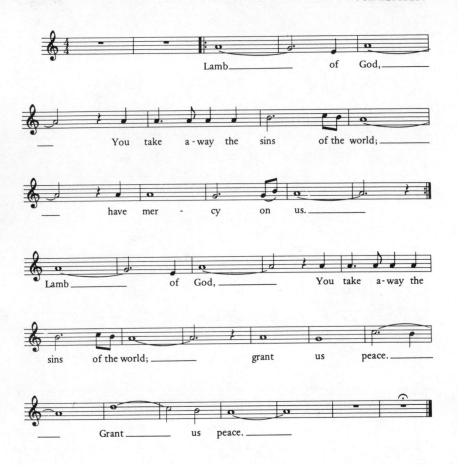

Lamb_____ of God,_____

_____ You take a-way the sins of the world;_____

_____ have mer - cy on us._____

Lamb_____ of God,_____ You take a-way the

sins of the world;_____ grant us peace._____

_____ Grant_____ us peace._____

Copyright © 1976 by North American Liturgy Resources, 10802 N. 23rd Avenue, Phoenix, Arizona, 85029.
All Rights Reserved.

All Our Joy

DARRYL DUCOTE

REFRAIN

All our joy,____ Lord, all our____ pain, all the times we've met You, __ Lord, __ we re-call a-gain. ____ Now we wish to show our__ love;__ through gifts we make it __ known. Take what we bring; make us__ Your own.

1.

2. own. **Last** 2. To own. ____

VERSES

1. Like the dew that car-pets dawn,__ Your love for us per-vades_
2. touch our hearts and make them feel __ that all the love You claim_

1. __ the morn __ and meets us at each corn-er, in each__
2. __ is real,__ You sent Your Son in laugh-ter and in__

1. smile. _____ And, though it ling-ers
2. tears. _____ But He not on-ly

1. through the day,__ our minds will turn and drift a-way.__ So
2. talked; He died.__ His bruis-es showed the love in-side.__ And

Copyright © 1970, 1979 by Damean Music. All Rights Reserved.

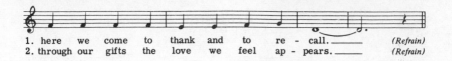

1. here we come to thank and to re - call. _____ (Refrain)
2. through our gifts the love we feel ap - pears. _____ (Refrain)

All That We Have

82

REFRAIN

GARY AULT

All that we have _____ and all that we of - fer _____

comes from a heart both fright - ened and free. _____

Take what we bring now and give what we need, _____

all done in His name.

VERSES

1. Some would re - ly on their pow - er, _____
2. Some - times the road may be lone - some, _____
3. Some - times when trou - bles are man - y, _____

1. oth - ers put trust in their gold. _____
2. of - ten we may lose our way; _____ take
3. life can seem emp - ty, it's true, _____ but

1. Some _____ have on - ly their Sav - ior, _____ whose
2. cour - age and al - ways re - mem - ber _____
3. look at the life of the Mas - ter, _____ who

1. faith - ful - ness nev - er grows old. _____ (Refrain)
2. love is - n't just for a day. _____ (Refrain)
3. lov - ing - ly suf - fered for you. _____ (Refrain)

Copyright © 1969, 1979 by Damean Music. All Rights Reserved.

83 Anthem

TOM CONRY

REFRAIN

We are called, we are cho-sen. We are Christ for one an-oth-er.

We are prom-ised to to-mor-row, while we are for Him to-day.

We are sign, we are won-der. We are sow-er, we are seed.

1. 2. 3.
We are har-vest, we are hun-gry. We are ques-tion, we are creed.

Last
ques-tion, we are creed.

VERSES

1. Then where can we stand jus - ti-fied? In what can we be-
2. Then how are we to stand at all, this world of bend-ed
3. Then shall we not stand emp-ty at the al-tar of our

1. lieve? In no one else but He Who suf-fered, no-thing
2. knee? In no-thing more than bar-ren sha-dows. No one
3. dreams? When He prom-ised us our-selves. Who mark

1. more than He Who rose. Who was jus-tice for the poor.
2. else but He could save us. Who was jus-tice for the poor.
3. time a-gainst to-mor-row. Who are jus-tice for the poor.

1. Who was rage a-gainst the night. Who was
2. Who was rage a-gainst the night. Who was
3. Who are rage a-gainst the night. Who are

1. 2.   *Last*
1. hope for peace-ful peo-ple. Who was light. *(Refrain)*
2. hope for peace-ful peo-ple. Who was light. *(Refrain)*
3. hope for peace-ful peo-ple. Who are light.

Copyright © 1978 by North American Liturgy Resources, Phoenix, Arizona 85029. All Rights Reserved.

Ashes

Introduction

TOM CONRY

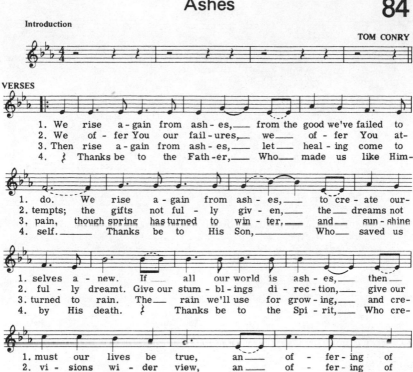

VERSES

1. We rise a-gain from ash-es,___ from the good we've failed to
2. We of-fer You our fail-ures,___ we___ of-fer You at-
3. Then rise a-gain from ash-es,___ let___ heal-ing come to
4. Thanks be to the Fath-er,___ Who___ made us like Him-

1. do. We rise a-gain from ash-es,___ to cre-ate our-
2. tempts; the gifts not ful-ly giv-en,___ the___ dreams not
3. pain, though spring has turned to win-ter,___ and___ sun-shine
4. self.___ Thanks be to His Son,___ Who___ saved us

1. selves a-new. If___ all our world is ash-es,___ then___
2. ful-ly dreamt. Give our stum-bl-ings di-rec-tion,___ give our
3. turned to rain. The___ rain we'll use for grow-ing,___ and cre-
4. by His death. Thanks be to the Spi-rit,___ Who cre-

1. must our lives be true, an___ of-fer-ing of
2. vi-sions wi-der view, an___ of-fer-ing of
3. ate the world a-new from an of-fer-ing of
4. ates the world a-new from an of-fer-ing of

| 1.2. | 3. | Last |

1. ash-es,___ an of-fer-ing to You.
2. ash-es,___ an of-fer-ing to You.
3. ash-es,___ an of-fer-ing to You.
4. ash-es,___ an of-fer-ing to You.___

Copyright © 1978 by North American Liturgy Resources, Phoenix, Arizona 85029. All Rights Reserved.

A Banquet Is Prepared

Based on Psalm 23

JOHN KAVANAUGH, S.J.

ANTIPHON

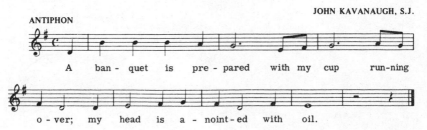

A ban-quet is pre-pared with my cup run-ning

o-ver; my head is a-noint-ed with oil.

Copyright © 1973 by John Kavanaugh, S.J.
Published exclusively by North American Liturgy Resources, Phoenix, Arizona 85029. All Rights Reserved.

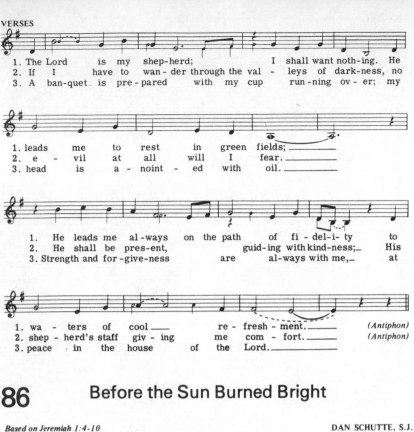

1. The Lord is my shep-herd; I shall want noth-ing. He
2. If I have to wan-der through the val - leys of dark-ness, no
3. A ban-quet. is pre-pared with my cup run-ning ov - er; my

1. leads me to rest in green fields; _____
2. e - vil at all will I fear. _____
3. head is a - noint - ed with oil. _____

1. He leads me al-ways on the path of fi - del-i- ty to
2. He shall be pres-ent, guid-ing with kind-ness;_ His
3. Strength and for -give-ness are al-ways with me,_ at

1. wa - ters of cool ____ re - fresh - ment. ____ (Antiphon)
2. shep - herd's staff giv - ing me com - fort. ____ (Antiphon)
3. peace in the house of the Lord. ____

86   Before the Sun Burned Bright

Based on Jeremiah 1:4-10

DAN SCHUTTE, S.J.

ANTIPHON

Be - fore the sun-burned bright and ri-vers flowed,

I called you each by name_ to share My home.

No long-er be a - fraid; I am your God.

My love will nev - er end._ Al - le - lu - ia.

Copyright © 1970 by Daniel L. Schutte, S.J.
Published exclusively by North American Liturgy Resources, Phoenix, Arizona 85029. All Rights Reserved.

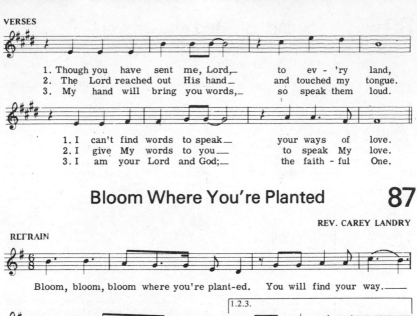

VERSES

1. Though you have sent me, Lord,— to ev - 'ry land,
2. The Lord reached out His hand— and touched my tongue.
3. My hand will bring you words,— so speak them loud.

1. I can't find words to speak— your ways of love.
2. I give My words to you— to speak My love.
3. I am your Lord and God;— the faith - ful One.

Bloom Where You're Planted 87

REV. CAREY LANDRY

REFRAIN

Bloom, bloom, bloom where you're plant-ed. You will find your way.——

1.2.3.

Bloom, bloom, bloom where you're plant-ed. You will have your day.——*(Verses)*

Last

You will have your day.——

VERSES

1. Look at the flow - ers, look at them grow - ing;
2. Some plant the seeds that oth - ers will wa - ter,
3. Look at the love that lies deep with - in you.

1. they nev - er wor - ry; they nev - er work; yet
2. but in all things—— God gives the growth.——
3. Let your self be! —— Let your - self be!——

1. look at the way—— our Fa - ther clothes them,
2. Come, let Him gar - den the flow - ers with - in you;
3. Look at the gifts—— you have been giv - en;

1. each with a beau - ty all of its own. *(Refrain)*
2. come and dis - cov - er some you've nev - er known. *(Refrain)*
3. Let them go free.—— Let them go free. *(Refrain)*

Copyright © 1979 by North American Liturgy Resources, Phoenix, Arizona 85029. All Rights Reserved.

88 Bread, Blessed and Broken

MICHAEL B. LYNCH

VERSES

1. Je - sus, You're the one — I love; You're the one I know. —
2. May the bread we break — to - day, May the cup we share —

1. — You're the one who makes — me strong,
2. — lift the bur - dens of — our hearts,

1. Spir - it in my soul. — From the clouds of yes -
2. lift them ev - 'ry-where; — pass-ing on to each —

1. — ter-day, through the night of pain, —
2. — of us a meas-ure of Your love, —

1. teach me, Lord, to know — Your way, know it once a - gain. —
2. love to make us whole — a - gain, as we share Your Word. —

REFRAIN

Bread blessed — and bro - ken for — us all, —

1.3.
sym-bol of Your love — from the grain so tall. —

2. Last
bread of life You give — to us, — bread of life for all. —

Copyright © 1978, 1979 by Raven Music. All Rights Reserved. Used with permission.

Choose Life

Based on Deuteronomy 30:15-20

REV. CAREY LANDRY

REFRAIN

O Lord, You came to bring us life, that we might have it more and more. We who share Your love, Your life, We choose life, choose life.

VERSE 1

1. You set be-fore us life or death: a bless-ing or a curse.___ We choose life that we may live in the land of the liv-ing for-ev-er.___ *(Refrain)*

VERSE 2

2. We choose life that our chil-dren may live and grow in the love of our God. Heed-ing His voice, we will cling to Him; we will share His life, His love for-ev-er.___ *(Refrain)*

Copyright © 1969, 1979 by Rev. Carey Landry
and North American Liturgy Resources, Phoenix, Arizona 85029. All Rights Reserved.

3. For it is You, Lord, that we choose; You, who bring a -

3. bun - dant life. To whom else, Lord, can we go?

3. You are the Way, the Truth, the Life. _____ *(Refrain)*

90   Come, Return to the Lord

Based on Hosea 6:1-3; 11:3,4

REV. CAREY LANDRY

REFRAIN

Come, _____ let us re - turn to the Lord! _____

_____ He will heal us; _____ He will heal; _____

_____ He will bind up our wounds. _____

VERSE 1

1. Long a - go He taught His peo - ple to walk. It is

1. He who held them in His arms, yet they did not know, ___ they

1. did not know _____ He had healed them. _____

VERSE 2

2. Like the rain He will come to us; like spring

2. rain wa - ter - ing the earth. He will lift us up; He will

2. raise us up that we may live! _____ *(Refrain)*

Copyright © 1979 by North American Liturgy Resources, Phoenix, Arizona 85029. All Rights Reserved.

VERSE 3

3. Our God will be God for us. That He will
3. come is as cer-tain as the dawn. Like a
3. mo-ther bend-ing o'er her child, our God is
3. ev-er near.___ *(Refrain)*

Come to Me, All Who Are Weary 91

Based on Matthew 11:28,25; 9:11-13; 18:1-4

DAN SCHUTTE, S.J.

ANTIPHON

Come un-to Me, all who are wea-ry and find rest for your soul.___

Come to Me, all who are bur-dened; you shall learn from Me.___

VERSE 1

1. Take My yoke up-on your shoul-ders; do not be a-fraid.___ For
1. I ___ will gent-ly teach you___ of the ways of the Lord.___*(Antiphon)*

VERSE 2

2. I have come not for the strong but for sin-ners frail;___ the
2. pow-er-less shall be fa-vored___ in the eyes of the Lord.___*(Antiphon)*

VERSE 3

3. You shall come to know se-cret things, hid-den from the wise.___ And
3. child-ren shall be ru-lers___ in the land of the Lord.___*(Antiphon)*

Copyright © 1972 by Daniel L. Schutte, S.J.
Published exclusively by North American Liturgy Resources, Phoenix, Arizona 85029. All Rights Reserved.

92 Come to the Water

Suggested by Isaiah 55:1,2; Matthew 11:28-30

JOHN FOLEY, S.J.

VERSES

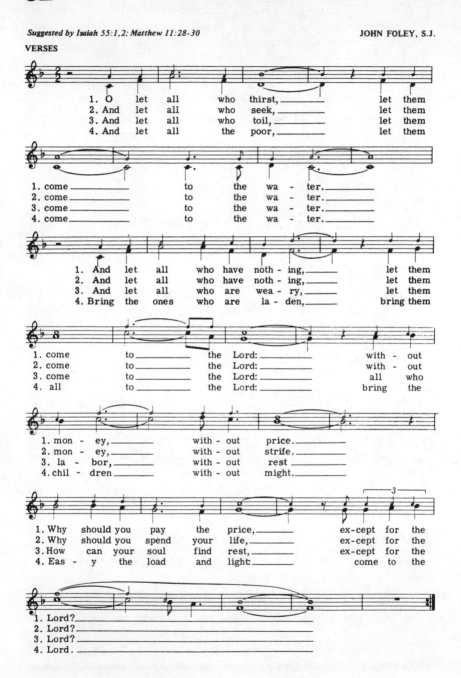

1. O let all who thirst, _____ let them
2. And let all who seek, _____ let them
3. And let all who toil, _____ let them
4. And let all the poor, _____ let them

1. come _____ to the wa - ter. _____
2. come _____ to the wa - ter. _____
3. come _____ to the wa - ter. _____
4. come _____ to the wa - ter. _____

1. And let all who have noth - ing, _____ let them
2. And let all who have noth - ing, _____ let them
3. And let all who are wea - ry, _____ let them
4. Bring the ones who are la - den, _____ bring them

1. come to _____ the Lord: _____ with - out
2. come to _____ the Lord: _____ with - out
3. come to _____ the Lord: _____ all who
4. all to _____ the Lord: _____ bring the

1. mon - ey, _____ with - out price. _____
2. mon - ey, _____ with - out strife. _____
3. la - bor, _____ with - out rest _____
4. chil - dren _____ with - out might. _____

1. Why should you pay the price, _____ ex - cept for the
2. Why should you spend your life, _____ ex - cept for the
3. How can your soul find rest, _____ ex - cept for the
4. Eas - y the load and light _____ come to the

1. Lord? _____
2. Lord? _____
3. Lord? _____
4. Lord. _____

Copyright © 1978 John B. Foley, S.J. and North American Liturgy Resources, Phoenix, Arizona 85029. All Rights Reserved.

The Cry of the Poor

Psalm 34:2,3; 17:18; 19:23

93

JOHN FOLEY, S.J.

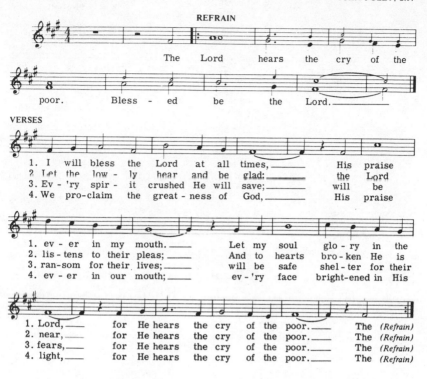

1. I will bless the Lord at all times, ___ His praise
2. Let the low - ly hear and be glad: ___ the Lord
3. Ev - 'ry spir - it crushed He will save; ___ will be
4. We pro-claim the great - ness of God, ___ His praise

1. ev - er in my mouth. ___ Let my soul glo - ry in the
2. lis - tens to their pleas; ___ And to hearts bro - ken He is
3. ran-som for their lives; ___ will be safe shel - ter for their
4. ev - er in our mouth; ___ ev - 'ry face bright-ened in His

1. Lord, ___ for He hears the cry of the poor. ___ The *(Refrain)*
2. near, ___ for He hears the cry of the poor. ___ The *(Refrain)*
3. fears, ___ for He hears the cry of the poor. ___ The *(Refrain)*
4. light, ___ for He hears the cry of the poor. ___ The *(Refrain)*

Copyright © 1978 John B. Foley, S.J. and North American Liturgy Resources, Phoenix, Arizona 85029. All Rights Reserved.

Dance in the Darkness

94

Refrain: Louise Collison
Verse 1: Psalm 126:6
Verse 2: John 16:21
Verse 3: 2 Corinthians 12:9,10

REV. CAREY LANDRY

Dance in the dark - ness, slow be the pace. Sur -
ren - der to the rhy - thm of re - deem - ing grace.

Copyright © 1977 by North American Liturgy Resources, Phoenix, Arizona 85029. All Rights Reserved.

137

1. Al-though you go forth weep - ing,
2. A wo-man in child - birth suf - fers be
3. Je - sus, Lord of weak - ness, we

1. car-ry ing the seed to be sown, you shall come back re -
2. cause her time has come. But when she holds her
3. wait in joy - ful hope. See our weak - ness,

1. joic - ing, car-ry -ing your sheaves full grown. *(Refrain)*
2. child in her arms her joy re - turns a - gain. *(Refrain)*
3. be our strength. Je - sus, be our light. *(Refrain)*

95 Do You Really Love Me?

Based on John 21:15-17

REV. CAREY LANDRY

VERSES

1. "Do you real - ly love Me?" Je -sus said to
2. "Do you real - ly love Me?" Je -sus said to
3. "Do you real - ly love Me?" Je -sus says to

1. Pe - ter. "Do you real - ly love Me?" Je -sus said a - gain.
2. Pe - ter. "Do you real - ly love Me?" Je -sus said a - gain.
3. me. "Do you real - ly love Me? Je -sus says to you.

1. "Yes, I real - ly love You," Pe - ter said with joy.
2. "Lord you know I love You," Pe - ter said with joy.
3. "Yes, we real - ly love You, we will fol - low You."

1. "Then feed My lambs," He said, — "Pe - ter, feed My lambs."
2. "Then feed My sheep," He said, — "Pe - ter, feed My sheep."
*3. "Then feed My lambs," He says; "My peo - ple, feed My sheep."

*Repeat three times.

Copyright © 1973 by Rev. Carey Landry and North American Liturgy Resources, Phoenix, Arizona 85029. All Rights Reserved.

Emanuel

TIM MANION

VERSE 1

1. Ba - by born in a stall.____ Long a - go now, and
1. hard to re - call. Cold wind, dark-ness and sin, your
1. wel - com-ing from us all.____ *(Verse 2)*

VERSE 2.

2. How can it be true?____ A world grown so old now, how
2. can it be new? Sor - row's end, God send,
2. born now for me and you. ____ *(Antiphon)*

ANTIPHON

E - man - u - el, E - man - u-
el, What are we that You have loved us so
well? A song on high, a Sav - ior's
nigh, an - gel hosts re - joice Thy glo -
ry____ to tell.

Copyright © 1977 by Timothy J. Manion and North American Liturgy Resources, Phoenix, Arizona 85029. All Rights Reserved.

VERSE 3

3. Lord, lead us to know._____ You lay like a

3. beg - gar, so hum - ble, so low; no place for Your

3. head and straw for a bed, the glo - ry of

3. God to show._____ *(Verse 4)*

VERSE 4

4. Babe on mo - ther's knee,_____ child so

4. soon to be nailed to a tree; all

4. praise, till the end of our days; O Lord, You have

4. set us free._____ *(Antiphon)*

97   Emmanuel

BUDDY CEASAR

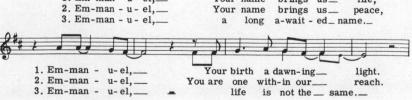

1. Em-man - u - el,___ Your name brings us___ life,
2. Em-man - u - el,___ Your name brings us___ peace,
3. Em-man - u - el,___ a long a-wait - ed_ name.__

1. Em-man - u - el,___ Your birth a dawn-ing___ light.
2. Em-man - u - el,___ You are one with-in our___ reach.
3. Em-man - u - el,___ life is not the__ same.__

Copyright © 1978 Damean Music. All Rights Reserved.

1. sent to us a ser-vant___ who lis-tens___ to our___
2. Your life guides our_____ way, Your love be-gins each___
3. A new___ age has___ dawned,___ Your dreams will lead us___

1. call, Em-man - u - el,___ God is with us___
2. day, Em-man - u - el,___ God is with us___
3. on. Em-man - u - el,___ God is with us___

1.2. Last

1. now.
2. now.

3. now.

3. Em-man - u - el,___ God is with us,___ Em-man-u - el.

Exult, You Just Ones

98

Based on Isaiah 40:3-5; Revelation 21:5

ROC O'CONNOR, S.J.

Pre-pare in the wil - der-ness___ a high - way

for our God!

VERSE 1

1. Pre-pare___ in the wil-der-ness___ a high-way for our God! Let

1. moun-tains and hills___ be made low;___ let the low - lands___ and

1. val - leys be raised!___ For the Lord re-veals His pow-er;___ the

1. Lord comes as a Lamb; the Lord is born as a man!___ *(Antiphon)*

Copyright © 1977 by Robert F. O'Connor, S.J.
and North American Liturgy Resources, Phoenix, Arizona 85029. All Rights Reserved.

ANTIPHON

Ex-ult you just ones in the Lord._____ Let hills and

moun-tains_ be sha-ken by your song, for the Lord walks a -

1.2.3. **Last**

mong us_ in our land._____ *(Verses)* land._____

VERSES 2 and 3

2. Yah-weh, the Might-y One,_ says this: "Be-hold,

2. I make all_things new. A new day has dawned for the na-tions_ of the

2. earth. Let all cre - a-tion re - joice!"_____ *(Antiphon)*

3. Yah-weh, the Ho - ly One,_says this: "I My-self

3. give you a sign: A vir-gin con - ceives and bears you a

3. Son. His name: E-man-u - el!"_____ *(Antiphon)*

99 Father of Peace

MICHAEL B. LYNCH

VERSES

1. Fa - ther of peace,_____ Fa - ther of
2. Fa - ther, we pray,_____ day af - ter

Copyright © 1976 by Raven Music. All Rights Reserved.

1. love, _____ come see our joy
2. day. _____ Help us to see

1. now, prais - ing Your Word. _____
2. You; show us Your way. _____

1. Fa - ther of life, _____ Fa - ther of
2. Fa - ther of care, _____ Guid - ing us

1. all, _____ Fa - ther of ev - 'ry -
2. all, _____ fill us with ev - 'ry -

1. thing that's good, we come to Your call. _____
2. thing that's good, we come to Your call. _____

Father, We Sing Your Praises 100

JOE ZSIGRAY

VERSES

1. We gath - er to - geth - er to wor - ship the Lord__ Who
2. In faith__ we come to Your ta - ble this day__ to
3. And in __ this meal__ we come__ to be __
4. We thank You, oh Lord, for the good - ness of life _____

1. out__ of love calls us to Him. And
2. cel - e - brate Your bread of life.
3. one in the bod - y that we share.
4. and for the love You show to us;

Copyright © 1979 by North American Liturgy Resources, Phoenix, Arizona 85029. All Rights Reserved.

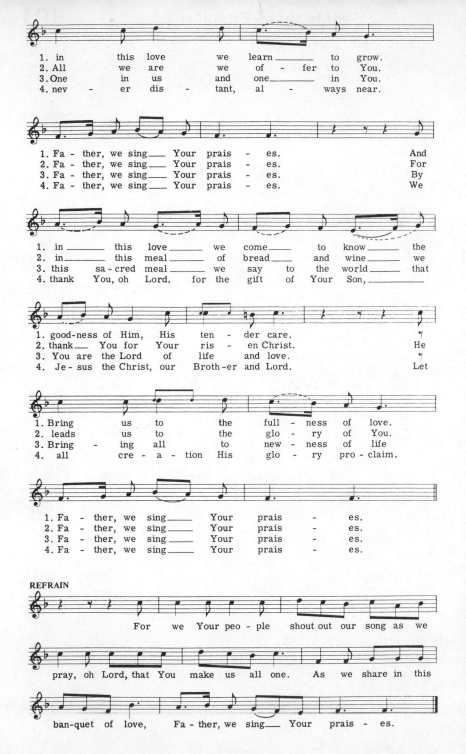

1. in this love we learn _____ to grow.
2. All we are we of - fer to You.
3. One in us and one_____ in You.
4. nev - er dis - tant, al - ways near.

1. Fa - ther, we sing_____ Your prais - es. And
2. Fa - ther, we sing_____ Your prais - es. For
3. Fa - ther, we sing_____ Your prais - es. By
4. Fa - ther, we sing_____ Your prais - es. We

1. in _____ this love_____ we come_____ to know_____ the
2. in_____ this meal_____ of bread_____ and wine_____ we
3. this sa - cred meal _____ we say to the world_____ that
4. thank You, oh Lord, for the gift of Your Son, _____

1. good-ness of Him, His ten - der care.
2. thank_ You for Your ris - en Christ. He
3. You are the Lord of life and love.
4. Je - sus the Christ, our Broth-er and Lord. Let

1. Bring us to the full - ness of love.
2. leads us to the glo - ry of You.
3. Bring - ing all to new - ness of life
4. all cre - a - tion His glo - ry pro - claim.

1. Fa - ther, we sing_____ Your prais - es.
2. Fa - ther, we sing_____ Your prais - es.
3. Fa - ther, we sing _____ Your prais - es.
4. Fa - ther, we sing_____ Your prais - es.

REFRAIN

For we Your peo - ple shout out our song as we

pray, oh Lord, that You make us all one. As we share in this

ban-quet of love, Fa - ther, we sing_ Your prais - es.

144

Get Me to the Promised Land 101

BOB FABING, S.J.

REFRAIN

Lead me on Lord, my Sav-ior. Lead me on
home, my Lord. Lead me on Lord, my Sav-ior.
Get me to the Prom-ised Land. Get me to the Prom-ised Land.

VERSES

1. The Lord will save His peo - ple, bro - thers.
2. The Lord walks on in tree - dom, sis - ters.
3. The Lord has called a meet - in' for glo - ry.
4. There'll be an - gels there just clap - pin' their hands.

1. Get me to the Prom-ised Land. So lift your heads and sing
2. Get me to the Prom-ised Land. So gath - er 'round and fol -
3. Get me to the Prom-ised Land. And there's no one here who's been
4. Get me to the Prom-ised Land. Then all God's chil-dren be - gin

1. His praise now. Get me to the Prom-ised Land. (Refrain)
2. low in His foot - steps. Get me to the Prom-ised Land. (Refrain)
3. for-got - ten. Get me to the Prom-ised Land. (Refrain)
4. to dance. Get me to the Prom-ised Land. (Refrain)

Copyright © 1977 by North American Liturgy Resources, Phoenix, Arizona 85029. All Rights Reserved.

God and Man at Table Are Sat Down 102

REV. ROBERT J. STAMPS

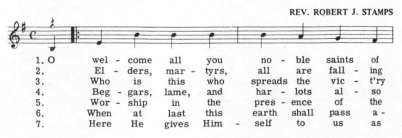

1. O wel - come all you no - ble saints of
2. El - ders, mar - tyrs, all are fall - ing
3. Who is this who spreads the vic - t'ry
4. Beg - gars, lame, and har - lots al - so
5. Wor - ship in the pres - ence of the
6. When at last this earth shall pass a -
7. Here He gives Him - self to us as

Copyright © 1979 by Dawn Treader Music (a division of Jubilee Communications, Inc.) Used by Permission. All Rights Reserved.

145

1. old,_____ as now be - fore your
2. down;_____ proph - ets, pa - tri -
3. feast?_____ Who is this who
4. here;_____ re - pen - tant pub - li -
5. Lord,_____ with joy - ful songs and
6. way,_____ when Je - sus and His
7. bread._____ Here as wine we

1. ver - y eyes un - fold_____ the won - ders all so
2. archs are gath-'ring round._____ What an - gels longed to
3. makes our war - ring cease?_____ Je - sus, ris - en
4. cans are draw - ing near;_____ way - ward ones come
5. hearts in one ac - cord,_____ and let our Host at
6. bride are one to stay,_____ the feast of love is
7. drink the blood He shed._____ Born to die, we

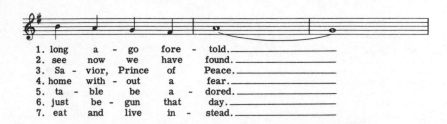

1. long a - go fore - told._____
2. see now we have found._____
3. Sa - vior, Prince of Peace._____
4. home with - out a fear._____
5. ta - ble be a - dored._____
6. just be - gun that day._____
7. eat and live in - stead._____

1. God and man at ta - ble are sat down._____
2. God and man at ta - ble are sat down._____
3. God and man at ta - ble are sat down._____
4. God and man at ta - ble are sat down._____
5. God and man at ta - ble are sat down._____
6. God and man at ta - ble are sat down._____
7. God and man at ta - ble are sat down._____

After Verse 7

God and man at ta - ble are sat down._____

146

His Love Will Ever Be 103

Based on Psalm 115

BOB FABING, S.J.

Praise Yah - weh, pro - claim Him, all you peo - ple. Sing His name, His love will ev - er be. Yah - weh comes with pow - er in His pres - ence. Sing His name, His love will ev - er be.

VERSES

1. Give thanks to Yah - weh, call His Name, ac - claim His deeds to all. Give glo - ry to His name and sing, you hearts that hear His call. Seek His strength and seek His face, re -
2. His rule is o - ver all the earth, His word is a com - mand. The pact He made with A - bra - ham, His oath to I - saac stand. He gave it as a law to Ja - cob,
3. He sent a man a - head of them, sold as a slave. Jo - seph's coat was i - ron chains till Yah - weh proved His fame. The king gave or - ders, set him free, and
4. His peo - ple bound by jeal - ous foes cried out with songs in prayer. And from the des - ert Mo - ses rose to fash - ion Yah - weh's care. He led his peo - ple from their midst, no
5. The bread of hea - ven from His hand strength - ened them each day. Wa - ter gushed from ar - id rocks to speed them on their way. Faith - ful to His sa - cred word to

Copyright © 1977 by North American Liturgy Resources, Phoenix, Arizona 85029. All Rights Reserved.

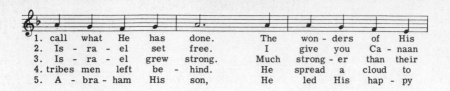

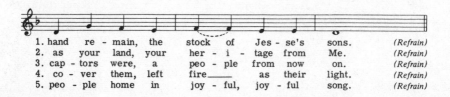

1. call what He has done. The won-ders of His
2. Is-ra-el set free. I give you Ca-naan
3. Is-ra-el grew strong. Much strong-er than their
4. tribes men left be-hind. He spread a cloud to
5. A-bra-ham His son, He led His hap-py

1. hand re-main, the stock of Jes-se's sons. *(Refrain)*
2. as your land, your her-i-tage from Me. *(Refrain)*
3. cap-tors were, a peo-ple from now on. *(Refrain)*
4. co-ver them, left fire as their light. *(Refrain)*
5. peo-ple home in joy-ful, joy-ful song. *(Refrain)*

104 I Have Loved You

Based on Jeremiah 31:3; Psalm 24:3

MICHAEL JONCAS

REFRAIN

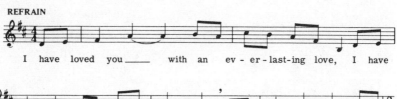

I have loved you____ with an ev-er-last-ing love, I have

called you____ and you are Mine;____ I have loved you____ with an

ev-er-last-ing love, I have loved you____ and you are Mine.

VERSES

1. Seek the face of the Lord and long for
2. Seek the face of the Lord and long for
3. Seek the face of the Lord and long for

1. Him:____ He will bring you His light and His peace.____
2. Him:____ He will bring you His joy and His hope.____
3. Him:____ He will bring you His care and His love.____

Copyright © 1979 by North American Liturgy Resources, Phoenix, Arizona 85029. All Rights Reserved.

REV. CAREY LANDRY

REFRAIN

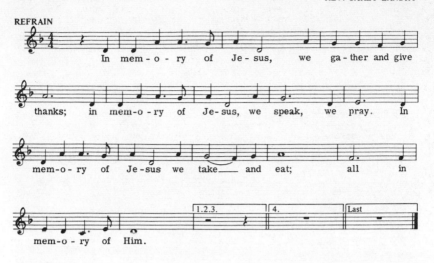

In mem-o-ry of Je-sus, we ga-ther and give thanks; in mem-o-ry of Je-sus, we speak, we pray. In mem-o-ry of Je-sus we take____ and eat; all in mem-o-ry of Him.

1.2.3.　　　4.　　　Last

VERSES 1 and 2

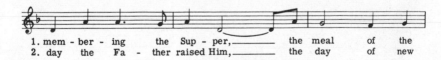

1. Re - mem - ber - ing　the man - na,　the hea - ven - ly bread;　re -
2. His mem - o - ry　is with us;　His mem - o - ry　is near:　the

1. mem - ber - ing　the day　　thou - sands were fed;　re -
2. day He died　to free us,____　the death that con-quered fear!____ The

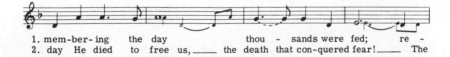

1. mem - ber - ing　the Sup - per,____　the meal　of the
2. day the Fa - ther raised Him,____　the day　of new

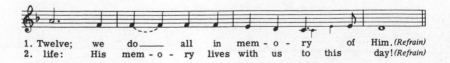

1. Twelve;　we do____ all　in mem - o - ry　of Him. *(Refrain)*
2. life:　His mem - o - ry　lives with us　to this　day! *(Refrain)*

Copyright © 1979 by North American Liturgy Resources, Phoenix, Arizona 85029. All Rights Reserved.

106
I Rejoiced

Based on Psalm 122:1, 2, 6-9

JOHN FOLEY, S.J.

1. I re-joiced when I heard them say:_____ we
2. For the sake of Je-ru-sa-lem,_____ pray
3. For the sake of our friends and kin,_____ pray

1. go to God's own home. And_____ now our feet have
2. peace be in our walls._____ And_____ peace be in our
3. peace be in our hearts._____ For the sake of His own

1. stood_____ with-in Your tem-ple, Lord._____
2. homes._____ May God's own good be known._____
3. home,_____ may God's own good be

[3.]

3. known,_____ in our hearts.

Alternate 3rd ending when sung as a round

3. known,_____ in our { land,_____ in our }
{ lives,_____ in our }
{ homes,_____ in our } hearts._____

*Use for singing as a four-part round.

Copyright © 1978 by John B. Foley, S.J. and North American Liturgy Resources, Phoenix, Arizona 85029. All Rights Reserved.

107
It's a Brand New Day

Based on Psalm 19

PAUL QUINLAN

1. It's a brand new_____ day, _____ ev-'ry-thing is_____
2. Well the hea-vens de-clare_____ in a way so_____
3. Well His law of love,_____ it is whol-ly_____

1. fine._____ Though it may be gray, I want you to
2. grand: _____ if the skies are fair or wind y or
3. wise._____ Word from a-bove gives joy to my

Copyright © 1975, 1979 by North American Liturgy Resources, Phoenix, Arizona 85029. All Rights Reserved.

1. know that the sun's gon-na shine;_____ and out of that
2. gray, it's the work of His hand._____ And down on the
3. heart, and it's light to my eyes._____ Its rich-es are

1. sky,_____ pierc-ing ev-er-y cloud_____
2. ground,_____ with nev-er a word,_____
3. fine,_____ out-last-ing all days._____

1. ____ is our God on high._____
2. ____ such a might-y sound._____
3. ____ till the end of time._____

1. There will be a new heart for ev-er-y man, like the flow-ers that
2. And the morn-ing will see the stroll-ing sun, as he hap-pi-ly
3. Though I walk in the path of e-vil ways, and my thoughts are a

1. come in ear-ly spring. For ev-er-y life there is_ a
2. ris-es o'er the land; a mes-sen-ger on his dail-y
3. pres-ence caus-ing pain, there is al-ways the sun of fu-ture

1. plan, no mat-ter what au-tumn breez-es bring.
2. run, bring-ing news of a Fath-er's guid-ing___ hand.
3. days, that fol-low the time of wind and___ rain.

REFRAIN

So put a-way care, let free-dom be

yours, joy is ev-er-y-where,_____ joy is ev-er-y-

where.___ Let free-dom ring, al-le-lu-ia now, ev-'ry-bod-y

sing, let our voi-ces shout to a might-y King!_____

151

108

Jesus Heal Us

RON ELLIS

VERSES

1. You search out our hearts___ and purge them with fire.___ You
2. To-geth-er we sense___ the Spir-it in song;___ Your

1. dwell deep in-side,___ in-creas-ing de-sire.___ Oh
2. Word cut-ting deep,___ we know we have wronged.__ Oh

1. Fa-ther,___ Fa-ther, why do we not feel___ the
2. Fa-ther,___ Fa-ther, why do we not heal?___ We

1. gift You do give___ so pure it is real?___
2. do we be-lieve,___ we need you to feel.___

REFRAIN

Je-sus, heal us. Spir-it,

free us. Je-sus, heal us.___

Copyright © 1974 by Raven Music. All Rights Reserved.

109

Jesus Is Our Prayer

RON ELLIS

VERSES

1. Qui-et___ times___ here and ev-'ry-where:___
   Hap-py are you___ in___ spir-it are poor,___
2. Hap-py are you___ who are hun-gry___ now,___
   Hap-py are you___ who___ weep___ now,___
3. Hap-py are you___ when re-ject-ed,___
   Qui-et___ times___ here and ev-'ry-where;___

1. peo-ple say,___ "Je-sus is our prayer."___
   for yours is___ the___ King-dom. (Refrain)
2. you shall be___ be___ sat-is-fied.___
   you shall laugh___ in___ all my joy.___ (Refrain)
3. for yours is___ the___ King-dom. (Refrain)
   peo-ple say,___ "Je-sus is our prayer." (Refrain)

Copyright © 1975 by Raven Music. All Rights Reserved.

REFRAIN

Fa - ther, You gave us Your Son.

In His Spir - it we live as one.

Jesus the Bread of Life 110

GRAYSON WARREN BROWN

REFRAIN

Je - sus, the Bread of life, Je - sus, the Bread of life. All who eat and drink of Him will nev - er die, will nev - er die.

VERSES

1. I am the Bread that came down from heav-en. I will be your food. All who put their trust in Me will nev - er die.
2. All who come to Me will not hun-ger, nor will they ev - er thirst. If you turn to Me in faith, I'll nev - er turn a - way.
3. All who love and keep My com-mand-ments will be loved by My Fa - ther. And we shall both com - fort them and make our home in them.

Copyright © 1979 by North American Liturgy Resources, Phoenix, Arizona 85029. All Rights Reserved.

111   Lead Us On, O Lord

REV. CAREY LANDRY

REFRAIN

Lead___ us on, O Lord, lead___ us on. Lead us
where we dare not go.___ Lead___ us on, O Lord,
lead___ us on. Be with___ us as we face new days.___

VERSES

1. All___ of our lives, O Lord, all of our dreams,
2. Fill___ us with strength, O Lord, fill us with hope.

1. All that we are and hope to be,___
2. Fill us with cour - age to go on.___

1. all of our strength is in our un - i - ty as one.
2. Filled with the sweet - ness of Your light and Your truth,

1. All our___ dan - ger is dis - cord.___ (Refrain)
2. We will___ find ways to share Your gift.___ (Refrain)

Copyright © 1971 by Rev. Carey Landry and North American Liturgy Resources, Phoenix, Arizona 85029. All Rights Reserved.

112   Let All the Earth

GARY AULT

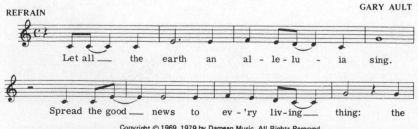

REFRAIN

Let all___ the earth an al - le - lu - ia sing.

Spread the good___ news to ev - 'ry liv - ing___ thing: the

Copyright © 1969, 1979 by Damean Music. All Rights Reserved.

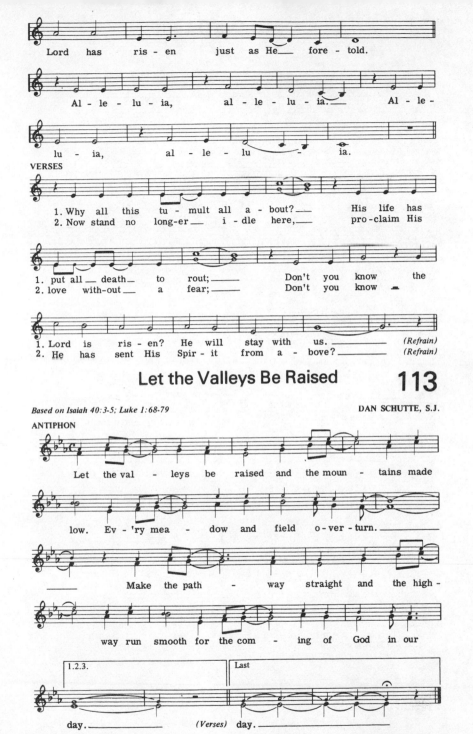

Lord has ris- en just as He fore- told.

Al- le- lu - ia, al- le- lu - ia. Al- le-

lu - ia, al- le- lu - ia.

VERSES

1. Why all this tu- mult all a- bout? His life has
2. Now stand no long-er i- dle here, pro-claim His

1. put all death to rout; Don't you know the
2. love with-out a fear; Don't you know

1. Lord is ris- en? He will stay with us. *(Refrain)*
2. He has sent His Spir- it from a- bove? *(Refrain)*

Let the Valleys Be Raised   113

Based on Isaiah 40:3-5; Luke 1:68-79   DAN SCHUTTE, S.J.

ANTIPHON

Let the val - leys be raised and the moun - tains made

low. Ev-'ry mea - dow and field o- ver- turn.

Make the path - way straight and the high-

way run smooth for the com - ing of God in our

1.2.3.   **Last**

day.   *(Verses)* day.

Copyright © 1977 by Daniel L. Schutte, S.J. and North American Liturgy Resource, Phoenix, Arizona 85029. All Rights Reserved.

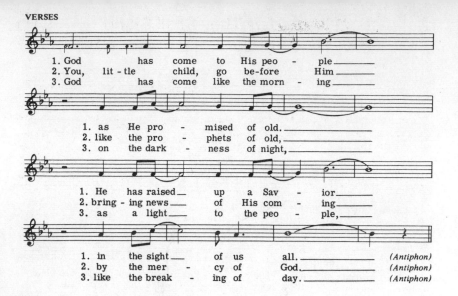

114   Like a Sunflower

REV. CAREY LANDRY

Copyright © 1979 by North American Liturgy Resources, Phoenix, Arizona 85029. All Rights Reserved.

Based on Psalm 92

DAN SCHUTTE, S.J.

ANTIPHON

I will play for Him on my harp,   with my lute and ten-stringed lyre.

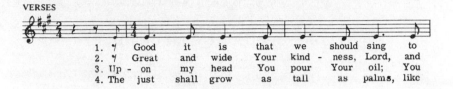

I will greet the Lord with my song;   I will sing of the

ways of the Lord.

VERSES

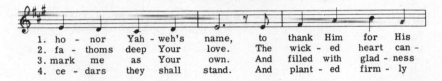

1. Good it is that we should sing to
2. Great and wide Your kind - ness, Lord, and
3. Up - on my head You pour Your oil; You
4. The just shall grow as tall as palms, like

1. ho - nor Yah - weh's name, to thank Him for His
2. fa - thoms deep Your love. The wick - ed heart can -
3. mark me as Your own. And filled with glad - ness
4. ce - dars they shall stand. And plant - ed firm - ly

1. love at dawn, His faith - ful - ness through night. *(Antiphon)*
2. not con - ceive; the fool - ish heart will fall. *(Antiphon)*
3. I shall sing; my horn shall sound Your call. *(Antiphon)*
4. on their God they shall not break nor bow. *(Antiphon)*

Copyright © 1972 by Daniel L. Schutte, S.J.
Published exclusively by North American Liturgy Resources, Phoenix, Arizona. All Rights Reserved.

Look Beyond   116

DARRYL DUCOTE

REFRAIN

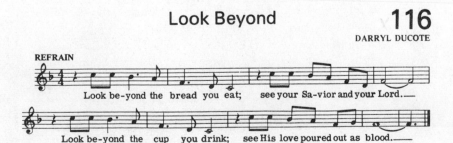

Look be-yond the bread you eat;   see your Sa-vior and your Lord.

Look be-yond the cup you drink;   see His love poured out as blood.

Copyright © 1969, 1979 by Damean Music. All Rights Reserved.

1. Give us a sign ___ that we might ___ be-lieve in you.
2. I am the bread ___ which from ___ the heav-ens came;
3. The bread I give you ___ will be ___ My ver-y flesh; My
4. This man speaks harsh-ly; who can lis - ten to His word?
5. You, My dis - ci -ples, ___ will you ___ al - so leave?

1. Mos - es gave us man - na from the sky. ___ (Refrain)
2. those who eat this bread will nev - er die. ___ (Refrain)
3. blood ___ will tru - ly be your drink. ___ (Refrain)
4. We ___ shall no long - er fol - low Him. ___ (Refrain)
5. Lord, ___ to whom ___ can we go? ___ (Refrain)

117   Lord, Send Out Your Spirit

JOE ZSIGRAY

REFRAIN

Lord, send out Your Spir - it, and re - new the
face of the earth. ___ earth. ___ (Verses)

VERSE 1

1. Bless ___ the Lord, oh ___ my soul. Oh
1. Lord, my God, You are great in - deed. ___
1. How man - i - fold are Your works, ___ oh Lord! ___ The
1. earth is full of Your crea - tures. ___ (Refrain)

Copyright © 1979 by North American Liturgy Resources, Phoenix, Arizona 85029. All Rights Reserved.

VERSE 2

2. If You take a-way their breath,___ oh

2. Lord, they die and re-turn to their dust.___

2.___ When You send forth Your Spir-it they live.___

2.___ You re-new the face of the earth.___ *(Refrain)*

VERSE 3

3. May the glo-ry of___ the Lord___ en -

3. dure for-ev-er,___ and may the

3. Lord be glad in His work.___

3. Pleas-ing to Him be my theme;___

3.___ for I re-joice in the Lord.___ *(Refrain)*

Lord, Today

118

MIKE BALHOFF
REFRAIN

DARRYL DUCOTE
GARY DAIGLE

Lord, to-day we have seen Your glo-ry, dawn

fol-lows the night. We, Your peo-ple who

walked in dark-ness now have seen a great light.___

Copyright © 1978 by Damean Music. All Rights Reserved.

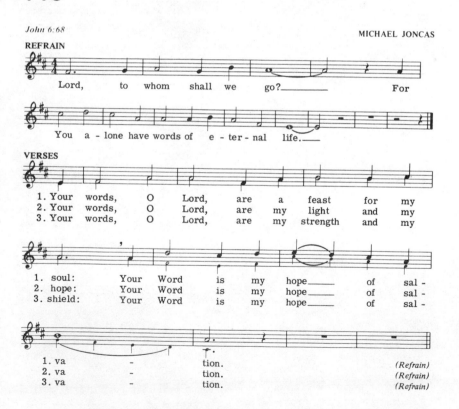

119 Lord, to Whom Shall We Go?

Copyright © 1979 by North American Liturgy Resources, Phoenix, Arizona 85029. All Rights Reserved.

Mighty Lord

120

Suggested by Psalms 86, 101, 148

JOHN FOLEY, S.J.

Copyright © 1978 by John B. Foley, S.J. and North American Liturgy Resources, Phoenix, Arizona 85029. All Rights Reserved.

161

121
Miracle of Life

RON ELLIS

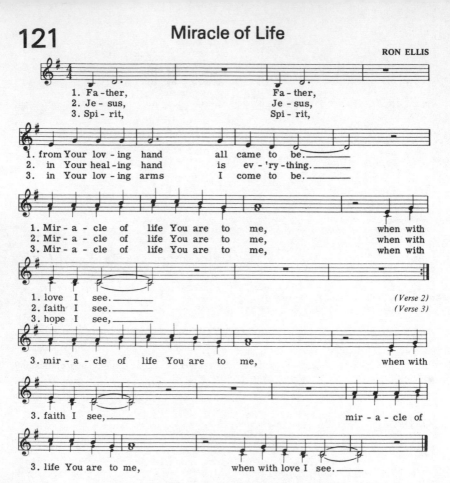

1. Fa-ther, Fa-ther,
2. Je-sus, Je-sus,
3. Spi-rit, Spi-rit,

1. from Your lov-ing hand all came to be.____
2. in Your heal-ing hand is ev-'ry-thing.____
3. in Your lov-ing arms I come to be.____

1. Mir-a-cle of life You are to me, when with
2. Mir-a-cle of life You are to me, when with
3. Mir-a-cle of life You are to me, when with

1. love I see.____ *(Verse 2)*
2. faith I see.____ *(Verse 3)*
3. hope I see.____

3. mir-a-cle of life You are to me, when with

3. faith I see,____ mir-a-cle of

3. life You are to me, when with love I see.____

Copyright © 1977, 1979 by Raven Music. All Rights Reserved. Used with permission.

122
Mountains and Hills

Based on Psalm 136

DAN SCHUTTE, S.J.

ANTIPHON

Come now to the Lord with your sing-ing and your danc-ing, with

trum-pets and gui-tars sound His praise.__ The moun-tains and the hills will re-

joice in your sing-ing; the ri-vers will clap their hands.

Copyright © 1971 by Daniel L. Schutte, S.J.
Published exclusively by North American Liturgy Resources, Phoenix, Arizona 85029. All Rights Reserved.

VERSES

1. Give thanks to Him for He is good, for His glory will
2. He it is who does great wonders; by His wisdon He
3. He is is who made the great lights, made the sun to rule
4. He led His people from their slav'ry and He kept them safe with

1. last for - ever. He is the Lord of lords.
2. made the heavens. He fashioned the land and the seas.
3. o'er the day, and the moon to mas - ter the night.
4. His own hand. He is the Lord of lords.

1.-4. For - e - ver will be His love. _____ *(Antiphon)*

My Soul Rejoices
(Magnificat)

123

Based on Luke 1:46-55

GARY AULT
MIKE BALHOFF
BUDDY CEASAR
DARRYL DUCOTE

REFRAIN

My soul re-joic - es in my God, my spi-rit pro-claims the

great-ness of the Lord. Ho-ly is His name.

VERSES

1. He has looked up - on His ser-vant in her low - li - ness.
2. He has shown to those who fear the Lord His might - y arm.
3. He has giv - en ev - 'ry good thing to the hung - ry ones,

1. Ev - 'ry age to come shall call me blest.
2. He con-fused the proud with - in their thoughts.
3. while He leaves the rich with emp - ty hands.

1. God who is might - y has done great things.
2. He has set down the might - y from their thrones,
3. He has been mind-ful of His mer - cy,

1. His mer - cy is from age to age. *(Refrain)*
2. and raised the low ly ones on high. *(Refrain)*
3. as He once pro-mised Ab - ra - ham. *(Refrain)*

Copyright © 1978 Damean Music. All Rights Reserved.

124 New Life

REV. CAREY LANDRY

REFRAIN

New life! New life! You came to bring us new life. New

life! New life! We find such joy in Your a-bun-dant life.

VERSES

1. You are the source of__ our great joy, the foun-tain of__ all
2. You are the source of__ our new life; in Your light we__ see

1. life. You give us liv-ing wa-ter; You bid us come and
2. light. You show to us__Your good-ness; You bid us taste and

1. drink. We come to You; we bless You, Lord; we
2. see. We come to You; we bless You, Lord; we

1. glor-i-fy__Your__ name! We praise You, Lord; we__ wor-ship You. We
2. glor-i-fy__Your__ name! We praise You, Lord; we__ wor-ship You. We

1. thank You for Your gift____ of new life! *(Refrain)*
2. thank You for Your gift____ of new life! *(Refrain)*

Copyright © 1975 by Rev. Carey Landry and North American Liturgy Resources, Phoenix, Arizona 85029. All Rights Reserved.

125 Night Is Over

Refrain based on Song of Songs 2:11-12

REV. CAREY LANDRY

VERSE 1

Soloist
1. Night is o-ver! Day____ is at hand! Christ our

1. light is ris en! Night is ov-er!

Copyright © 1979 by North American Liturgy Resources, Phoenix, Arizona 85029. All Rights Reserved.

1. Day ___ is at hand! Dark - ness has been ov - er -

1. come ___ for - ev - er! ___

REFRAIN

And lo! the win - ter is past! ___ Rains are o - ver and gone!

Earth, on the earth.

Flow - ers ap - pear ___ on the earth! ___

Lo! the win - ter is past! Rains are o - ver and gone! Glad songs!

Fine

Glad songs are heard! ___

VERSES 2 and 3

2. God has raised up Je - sus! ___ His
3. Christ our light is ris - en! ___

2. splen - dor shines forth through - out ___ the earth!
3. We are His faith - ful wit - ness - es.

2. God has raised up Je - sus! ___ The hea - vens de - clare His
3. Christ our light is ris - en! ___ Let us re - joice! Oh!

2. tri - umph o'er death for - ev - er! ___ *(Refrain)*
3. Let us re - joice for - ev - er! ___ *(Refrain)*

165

126   On Eagle's Wings

Based on Psalm 91

MICHAEL JONCAS

VERSE 1

1. You who dwell in the shel-ter of the Lord, who a-
1. bide in His shad-ow for life, say to the Lord: "My
1. ref - uge, my Rock in whom I trust!" *(Refrain)*

REFRAIN

And He will raise you up on ea-gle's wings, bear you on the
breath of dawn, make you to shine— like the sun,——— and
hold you in— the— palm——— of His hand.———

After Last Refrain

And hold you, hold you in the palm——— of His hand.———

VERSE 2

2. The snare of the fowl-er will nev-er cap-ture you, and
2. fam-ine will bring you no fear:— un-der His wings your
2. ref - uge,— His faith-ful-ness—— your shield. *(Refrain)*

Copyright © 1979 by North American Liturgy Resources, Phoenix, Arizona 85029. All Rights Reserved.

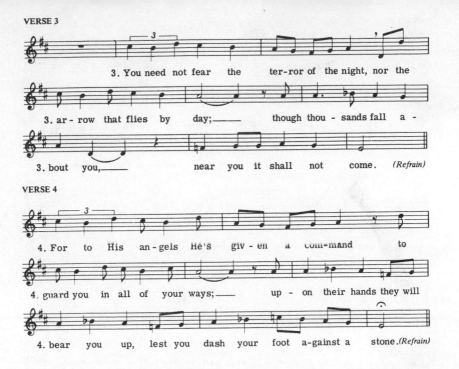

3. You need not fear the ter-ror of the night, nor the

3. ar-row that flies by day;___ though thou-sands fall a-

3. bout you,___ near you it shall not come. *(Refrain)*

VERSE 4

4. For to His an-gels He's giv-en a com-mand to

4. guard you in all of your ways;___ up-on their hands they will

4. bear you up, lest you dash your foot a-gainst a stone.*(Refrain)*

One Bread, One Body   127

Based on 1 Corinthians 10:16,17; 12:4;
Galatians 3:28
The Didache 9   JOHN FOLEY, S.J.

REFRAIN

One bread,___ one bod-y, one Lord of

all,___ one cup of bless-ing which we

bless.___ And we,___ though man-y,___

___ through-out the earth,___ we are one

bod-y in this one___ Lord.___ *(Verses)*

Copyright © 1978 by John B. Foley, S.J. and North American Liturgy Resources, Phoenix, Arizona 85029. All Rights Reserved.

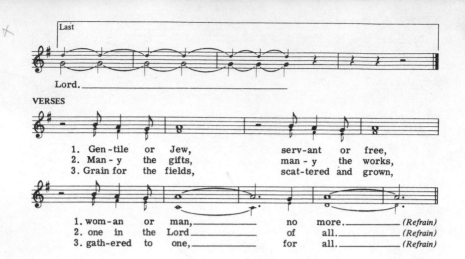

Last

Lord.

VERSES

1. Gen-tile   or   Jew,   serv-ant   or   free,
2. Man-y   the   gifts,   man-y   the   works,
3. Grain for   the   fields,   scat-tered and   grown,

1. wom-an   or   man,_____   no   more._____ *(Refrain)*
2. one   in   the   Lord_____   of   all._____ *(Refrain)*
3. gath-ered   to   one,_____   for   all._____ *(Refrain)*

128   Only in God

Based on Psalm 62:1,2,8,11,12

JOHN FOLEY, S.J.

ANTIPHON

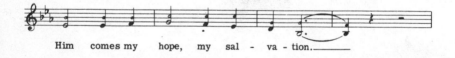

On - ly   in   God will my   soul   be   at   rest.____ From

Him   comes my   hope,   my   sal - va - tion._____

He   a - lone   is   my   rock   of   safe - ty,   my

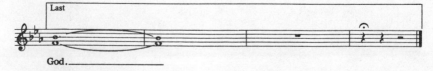

1.2.

strength,   my   glo - ry,   my   God._____   *(Verse)*

Last

God.

Copyright © 1976 by John B. Foley, S.J. and North American Liturgy Resources, Phoenix, Arizona 85029. All Rights Reserved.

VERSES

1. Trust in Him at all times, O peo - ple, and
2. Man - y times have I heard Him tell of His

1. pour out _____ your hearts. God Him -
2. long last - ing love. _____ You Your-

1. self is a re - fuge for us and a
2. self, Lord, re - ward all who la - bor for

1. strong - hold _____ for our fear. _____ *(Antiphon)*
2. love of _____ Your name. _____ *(Antiphon)*

Our Blessing Cup

129

Refrain: 1 Corinthians 10:16
Vs. 1: Psalm 116:12,13
Vs. 2: Psalm 34:9a
Vs. 3: 1 Corinthians 11:26

MICHAEL JONCAS

REFRAIN

Our_ bless-ing cup_ is a com-mu-nion_ in the

1.3.5.7. | 2.4.6. | Last

blood of Christ._ Christ._

VERSE 1

1. How shall I make_ a re - turn _____ to the Lord for

1. all the good_ He has done for me?_ The

mf

1. cup of sal - va - tion I will take up,_ and I will

Copyright © 1979 by North American Liturgy Resources, Phoenix, Arizona 85029. All Rights Reserved.

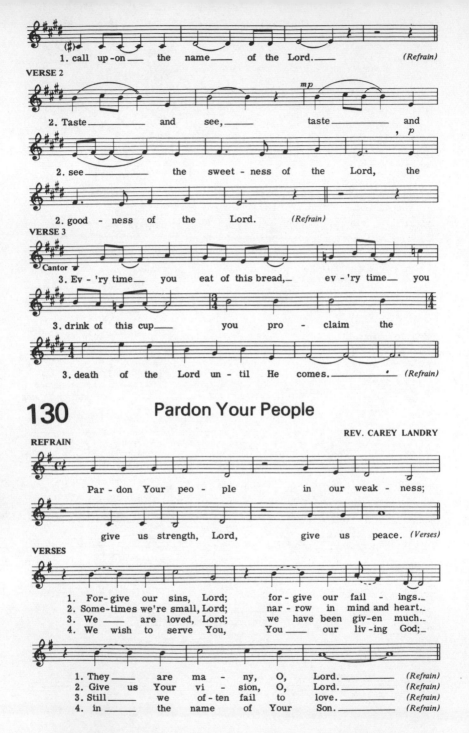

1. call up-on___ the name___ of the Lord.___ *(Refrain)*

VERSE 2

2. Taste___ and see, taste___ and

2. see___ the sweet - ness of the Lord, the

2. good - ness of the Lord. *(Refrain)*

VERSE 3

Cantor

3. Ev - 'ry time___ you eat of this bread,___ ev - 'ry time___ you

3. drink of this cup___ you pro - claim the

3. death of the Lord un - til He comes.___ *(Refrain)*

130 Pardon Your People

REV. CAREY LANDRY

REFRAIN

Par - don Your peo - ple in our weak - ness;

give us strength, Lord, give us peace. *(Verses)*

VERSES

1. For - give our sins, Lord; for - give our fail - ings.___
2. Some - times we're small, Lord; nar - row in mind and heart.___
3. We___ are loved, Lord; we have been giv - en much.___
4. We wish to serve You, You___ our liv - ing God;___

1. They___ are ma - ny, O, Lord.___ *(Refrain)*
2. Give us Your vi - sion, O, Lord.___ *(Refrain)*
3. Still___ we of - ten fail to love.___ *(Refrain)*
4. in___ the name of Your Son.___ *(Refrain)*

Copyright © 1979 by Rev. Carey Landry and North American Liturgy Resources, Phoenix, Arizona 85029. All Rights Reserved.

Patience, People

Based on James 5:7-9,11

JOHN FOLEY, S.J.

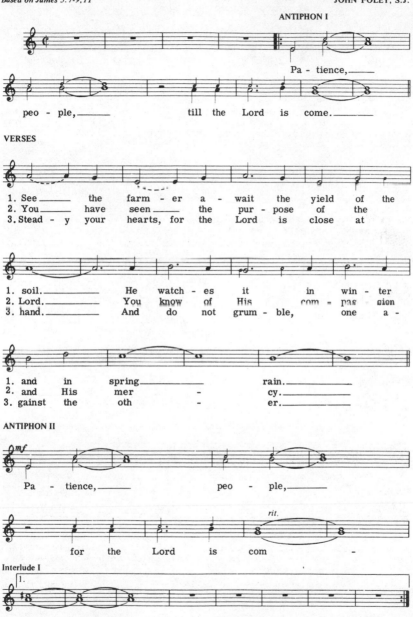

ANTIPHON I

Pa - tience,____ peo - ple,____ till the Lord is come.____

VERSES

1. See____ the farm - er a - wait the yield of the
2. You____ have seen____ the pur - pose of the
3. Stead - y your hearts, for the Lord is close at

1. soil.____ He watch - es it in win - ter
2. Lord.____ You know of His com - pas - sion
3. hand.____ And do not grum - ble, one a -

1. and in spring____ rain.____
2. and His mer - cy.____
3. gainst the oth - er.____

ANTIPHON II

mf

Pa - tience,____ peo - ple,____

rit.

for the Lord is com -

Interlude I

1.

ing.____

(Antiphon I)

Copyright © 1977 by John B. Foley, S.J. and North American Liturgy Resources, Phoenix, Arizona 85929. All Rights Reserved.

132 Paul's Prayer

Based on Ephesians 3

BOB FABING, S.J.

1. This is what I pray for from our Fa - ther's hand.
2. May He give you pow - er for your hid - den self
3. You will have the strength, then, build - ing now on love,
4. Glo - ry be whose pow er work - ing in us now

1. From Him ev - 'ry fam - ily takes its life and its
2. to grow strong, grow strong that Christ may live in your
3. strength to grasp the length and breadth, the height and the
4. can do more than we can ask or we can im -

1. name. Out of His glo - ry may He give to
2. hearts. Then through faith in Him plant - ed deep in
3. depth, un - til know - ing Christ's love which is be - yond all
4. a - gine. Glo - ry be to Him, then; age to age His

1. you pow - er through His Spir - it pre - sent
2. love, you will know with all the saints His
3. know - ing, you are filled with ut - ter full - ness
4. praise be in His church and in Christ Je - sus.

1.2.3. | **Last**

1. al - ways.
2. glo - ry.
3. God's love.
4. A - men. A - men.

Copyright © 1977 by North American Liturgy Resources, Phoenix, Arizona 85029. All Rights Reserved.

133 The People That Walk in Darkness

Based on Isaiah 9

BOB DUFFORD, S.J.

1. The peo - ple that walk in dark - ness have

1. seen, have seen a great light. And on those who

1. dwell in end - less gloom, a light has shone.

Copyright © 1977 by Robert J. Dufford, S.J. and North American Liturgy Resources, Phoenix, Arizona 85029. All Rights Reserved.

ANTIPHON

For a Child is born this day: Re-joice, re - joice.

Daugh-ter of Zi - on, a - wake! The glo-ry of God is

1. born. (Verse 2) 2. born. (Verse 3)

3. born. (Verse 4) Last born. Fine

VERSE 2

2. And they shall name Him coun-sel-or, shall call Him might-y

2. God. And He shall rule from age to age: Prince of peace. (Antiphon)

VERSE 3

3. Dark - ness cov-ers the earth; thick clouds

3. gov-ern its peo-ple, but the Lord will bring them

3. light. The Lord will bring them light. (Antiphon)

VERSE 4

4. The peo - ple that walk in dark - ness have

4. seen, have seen a great light. And on those who

4. dwell in end - less gloom a light has shone. (Antiphon)

173

134 Remember Your Love

MIKE BALHOFF

DARRYL DUCOTE
GARY DAIGLE

REFRAIN

Re - mem - ber Your love__ and Your faith- ful- ness, O Lord. Re- mem- ber Your peo- ple and have mer- cy on us, Lord. Lord.

1.2.3.4.5. || Last | Fine

VERSES

1. The Lord is my light and my sal - va - tion; whom should I
2. If You dwelt,__ O Lord, up - on our sin - ful - ness, then who could
3. O Lord, hear the sound__ of my call__ and an - swer
4. As watch - man who waits up - on the day - light, wait for the
5. Be - fore all the moun-tains were be - got - ten and earth took

1. fear? The Lord is my life__ and my
2. stand? But with You there is mer - cy and for -
3. me. My heart cries__ out__ for Your
4. Lord. I trust in His kind - ness and re -
5. shape, e - ven then,__ O Lord, You were our

1. re - fuge; when I call He hears.__ (Refrain)
2. give - ness and a guid - ing hand.__ (Refrain)
3. pres - ence; it is You I seek.__ (Refrain)
4. demp - tion; and His faith - ful word.__ (Refrain)
5. re - fuge through-out ev - 'ry age.__ (Refrain)

Copyright © 1978 Damean Music. All Rights Reserved.

135 Sacrament

VERSES 1, 2 and 4

REV. CAREY LANDRY

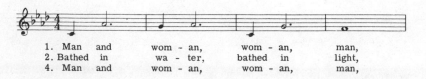

1. Man and wom - an, wom - an, man,
2. Bathed in wa - ter, bathed in light,
4. Man and wom - an, wom - an, man,

Copyright © 1979 by North American Liturgy Resources, Phoenix, Arizona 85029. All Rights Reserved.

1. bro - ther, sis - ter, hand in hand;
2. sight a - noint - ed, touched with oil;
4. one for - ev - er, hand in hand;

1. Called to lis - ten, called to speak
2. Ta - ble cen - tered, ta - ble fed,
4. One in vi - sion, heart and mind,

1. wound - ed heal - ers, ho - ly, weak.
2. Word to wit - ness, Spir - it led.
4. heal - ing pres - ence, gen - tle, kind.

REFRAIN

Je - sus, Shep - herd, Je - sus, Lord.

Let our lives rise like **leav - en;** be -

come as bread, _____ bro - ken and shared,

lives laid down for each oth - er in

1. Last   *Fine*   2.

love. _____   *(Verse 2)*   *(Verse 3)*

VERSE 3

3. For where two or three _____ are

3. gath - ered in Your name, _____ there

3. al - so are You! _____ There al - so are

3. You! _____   *(Verse 4)*

175

136 Service

VERSES

BUDDY CEASAR

1.4. We are made for serv-ice___ to care for each oth-er
2. God___ sent His Son___ to show us the way,___
3. Life can be so lone-ly___ when no-bod-y cares;___

1.4. we are made to love___ each___ sis - ter and broth-er with___
2. one who shared His love___ ev-'ry min-ute_ of the day,___
3. life can be so emp-ty when no - bod-y shares but if

1.4. love that will last through sor- row and pain, a
2. one who gave His life that we might live and His
3. we give our-selves both time and a - gain the

1.4. love_____ that will nev-er___ die with strain. *(Verse 2)*
2. Spir-it_____ to help us ___ through the years. *(Verse 3)*
3. hap-pi - ness of Christ will live with - in. *(Verse 4)*

Copyright © 1969, 1979 by Damean Music. All Rights Reserved.

137 Shalom

DONALD J. REAGAN

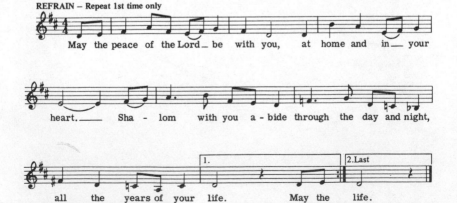

REFRAIN – Repeat 1st time only

May the peace of the Lord_ be with you, at home and in ___ your

heart.___ Sha - lom with you a - bide through the day and night,

1. all the years of your life. 2.Last May the life.

Copyright © 1979 by North American Liturgy Resources, Phoenix, Arizona 85029. All Rights Reserved.

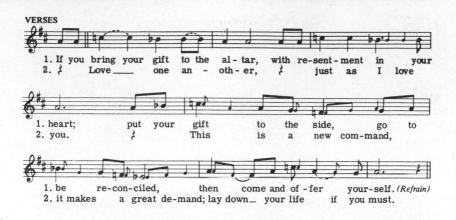

1. If you bring your gift to the al - tar, with re-sent-ment in your
2. ⎨ Love___ one an - oth - er, ⎨ just as I love

1. heart; put your gift to the side, go to
2. you. ⎨ This is a new com-mand,

1. be re-con-ciled, then come and of - fer your-self. *(Refrain)*
2. it makes a great de-mand; lay down___ your life if you must.

Shepherd's Alleluia 138

JACK JAWORSKI
REV. CAREY LANDRY

REFRAIN

The Lord is our Sav - ior and Shep-herd.___ Al - le -

lu - ia!___ He knows His own and He

leads us to life! Al - le - lu - ia.___

VERSES

1. With eyes dark and stumb - ling we grope in the
2. For the Lord was___ raised on Eas - ter___
3. We fol - low in glad - ness, we fol - low in
4. We fol - low the Lord in all that we

1. night, al - le - lu - ia.___ But He knows His
2. morn: al - le - lu - ia.___ To raise us with
3. pain; al - le - lu - ia.___ With love for each
4. do; al - le - lu - ia.___ We trust in His

1. own and He leads us to light. Al - le - lu - ia.___ *(Refrain)*
2. Him to___ new-ness of life. Al - le - lu - ia.___ *(Refrain)*
3. oth - er we fol-low a - gain. Al - le - lu - ia.___ *(Refrain)*
4. glo - ry to see us___ through. Al - le - lu - ia.___ *(Refrain)*

Copyright © 1969, 1979 by Rev. Carey Landry
and North American Liturgy Resources, Phoenix, Arizona 85029. All Rights Reserved.

139 Sing Out His Goodness

DARRYL DUCOTE

REFRAIN

Sing out His good-ness with your life.

Chant forth His praise by your love de - spite all strife,

day by day come what may,

day by day.

VERSES

1. As a light in dark - ness,
2. Through the warmth of friend - ship,
3. In your con - stant kind - ness,
4. To those bent in fail - ure,
5. By your self - less giv - ing,

1. as a cit - y on a hill,
2. through the trust - ing shared be - tween,
3. in the par - dons that you give,
4. to the peo - ple in de - spair,
5. by your help - ing those in need,

1. show His love to all as He would will. (Refrain)
2. all will see what faith in Him might mean. (Refrain)
3. you can show His long - ing to for - give. (Refrain)
4. by your help you show that God does care. (Refrain)
5. His true love will shine through you in - deed. (Refrain)

Copyright © 1969, 1979 by Damean Music. All Rights Reserved.

Sing to God a Brand New Canticle 140

Psalm 149

PAUL QUINLAN

REFRAIN

Sing to God a brand new, brand new can - ti - cle and
fill the val - leys with a new song, Fill the val - leys, yes, and
go fill the cit - ies too, and sing the an - cient al - le - lu.

VERSES

1. Is - ra - el, let your joy be God and
2. For the Lord is a God of love, Come to
3. For the Lord is a King of kings, God on

1. sing: Praise the Lord in ev - 'ry thing, Al - le -
2. free all the poor with vic - to - ry, Al - le -
3. high in whose love we'll nev - er die, Al - le -

1. lu - ia, praise the Lord,____ and let the na - tions
2. lu - ia, praise the Lord,____ and let the na - tions
3. lu - ia, praise the Lord,____ and let the na - tions

1. shout, and clap their hands for joy. Let the
2. shout, and clap their hands for joy. Let the
3. shout, and clap their hands for joy. Let the

1. na - tions shout and clap their hands for
2. na - tions shout and clap their hands for
3. na - tions shout and clap their hands for

1.2.   D.C. Last   Fine

1. joy._____ (Refrain)
2. joy._____ (Refrain)
3. joy.____

Words and music copyright © 1970 by Paul Quinlan. All Rights Reserved.

141 Sing to the Lord

MIKE BALHOFF

DARRYL DUCOTE
GARY DAIGLE

Melody
Sing to the Lord a new song;—
raise your voic - es,— all— you na - tions.
Sing to the Lord a new song;—

1.2.3.
join the hymn— of— all— cre - a - tion. *(Verses)*

Fine
cre - a - tion,— Ooo.—

VERSES

1. Praise the Lord,— praise Him glad - ly in the heights;—
2. Fire and hail— and the winds that sweep the earth;—
3. Praise His name— for the won - ders He has done;—

1. — praise Him, all you an - gels, come to
2. — praise Him, all you moun - tains, chant His
3. — all the peo - ples praise— Him, for the

1. sing out, all you hosts.— Sun and moon,— praise Him,
2. great - ness, all you hills.— Sing His love,— all you
3. Lord a - lone is great.— Is - ra - el,— sing out

1. all you shin - ing stars,— let them praise His good-
2. crea - tures of the land,— ga - ther all cre - a -
3. all this faith - ful - ness,— let them lift their voi-

1. ness,— His love shall— be— for - ev - er. *(Refrain)*
2. tion,— pro - claim His— word to - geth - er. *(Refrain)*
3. ces— with joy - ful— al - le - lu - ias. *(Refrain)*

Copyright © 1978 by Damean Music. All Rights Reserved.

Song of Jesus Christ 142

Based on Philippians 2:5-11

JOHN SHEEHAN
Arr. by Rev. Carey Landry

REFRAIN

Deep with-in us, shared a-mong us, may we ev-er keep the mind and heart of Je-sus Christ.___ ___ 2. He / 5. So

VERSES

1. Though He was at one with___ God, He did not think He should re-tain e-qual-i-ty with God, with God.___ (Refrain)
2. gave Him-self, He emp-tied Him-self, and took the na-ture of a slave, to be a man like us, like us.___ (Refrain)
3. He be-came more hum-ble yet, for He ac-cep-ted ev-en death, a death up-on a cross, a cross.___ (Refrain)
4. There-fore God raised Him to the heights and gave Him the name a-bove all names, in heav-en and on earth, on earth.___ (Refrain)
5. at His name all knees should___ bend and ev-'ry tongue___ pro-claim that Je-sus Christ is Lord, is Lord.___ (Refrain)

Copyright © 1969 by Theological College.
Copyright © 1975 by North American Liturgy Resources, Phoenix, Arizona 85029. All Rights Reserved.

Song of Thanksgiving 143

JOE ZSIGRAY

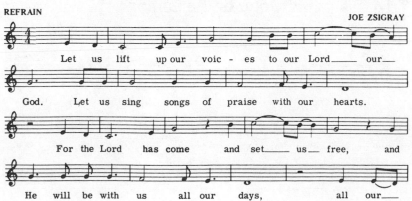

REFRAIN

Let us lift up our voic-es to our Lord___ our___ God. Let us sing songs of praise with our hearts. For the Lord has come and set___ us___ free, and He will be with us all our days, all our___

Copyright © 1973 by North American Liturgy Resources, Phoenix, Arizona 85029. All Rights Reserved.

1.2.

Last

days.___ days.

VERSE 1

1. Do not be a-fraid,___ for I am___ with___

1. you. I call you by your name and you are Mine.___

1. ___ If you___should be-come dis-tressed___ I will be with you,___

1. ___ and if you be-come sad, I will be your joy. *(Refrain)*

VERSE 2

2. Go forth in peace___ and make dis - ci - ples of all

2. na-tions;___ bap - tiz - ing them in My name,___

2. and teach them to love one an - oth - er; and re -

2. mem-ber that I'll be with you ev - 'ry___ day.___ *(Refrain)*

144 Song of the Lamb

BOB FABING, S.J.

REFRAIN

Lamb of God___ al - le - lu - ia,___

al - le - lu - ia,___ al - le - lu - ia.___ Lamb of God___

___ al - le - lu - ia,___ al - le - lu - ia.

Copyright © 1977 by North American Liturgy Resources, Phoenix, Arizona 85029. All Rights Reserved.

Son of David   145

Based on Mark 10:47,48;
Psalm 34:6,10; 126:5;
Isaiah 11:6,7; 53:1,4,9

JOHN FOLEY, S.J.

VERSES

1. 𝄽 On that night ____ You took the bread and
2. 𝄽 Then You took the cup at ta - ble,
3. 𝄽 On the hill ____ You took the cup Your
4. In days of old, ____ the He - brew priest would
5. And so, our Fa - ther, we of - fer You this

1. blessed and broke ____ Your life up - on the earth to save us
2. blessed and shared ____ with Your dis - ci - ples Your new pro - mise
3. Fa - ther gave You and poured Your life blood down the years in -
4. hold our lamb ____ to You on high; now You have giv - en
5. liv - ing bread, ____ our lamb for You, this sav - ing cup for

1. and to raise us to Your Fa - ther's throne. *(Refrain)*
2. in Your blood that You would set us free. *(Refrain)*
3. to our hearts, that none of us be lost. *(Refrain)*
4. Your own pres - ence as our of - fer - ing. *(Refrain)*
5. our sal - va - tion, sure to set us free. *(Refrain)*

REFRAIN

Son of Da - vid, have pit - y on me;
Son of God, hear my plea. O, Son of Da - vid, have
pit - y on me; lis - ten to my plea. ____

VERSES 1 – 3

1. Those who sow in tears and pain will re -
2. He has borne our grief and pain,
3. By His word this world was made, ev - 'ry

1. turn re - joic - ing. ____ The Lamb will leap, the
2. down with sor - row. ____ Who'd be - lieve what
3. grain and flow - er. ____ The poor stand near to

D.S.

1. lion lie down, on Your day, O Lord. ____ *(Refrain)*
2. we have seen? Like a lamb He's slain. ____ *(Refrain)*
3. God, the Lord: those who seek His face. ____ *(Refrain)*

Copyright © 1978 by John B. Foley, S.J. and North American Liturgy Resources, Phoenix, Arizona 85029. All Rights Reserved.

VERSE 4

4. Lord God, bring us back. Let Thy

4. face shine up-on us. Turn a-gain, see this

4. vine which Thine hand has plant-ed. *(Last Refrain)*

146   Speak, Lord

GARY AULT

REFRAIN

Speak, Lord, I'm list-'ning, plant Your word down deep in me:

Speak, Lord, I'm list-'ning, please show me the way. *(Verses)*

VERSES

1. Some-times my heart is slow to fol-low You;
2. Some-times I stum-ble on my way to You;

1. teach me to hear and un-der-stand; and I'm
2. stretch out a-gain Your heal-ing hand; and I'm

1.2. told the things You pro-mise, and I hope they all come true, and I

1.2. know what waits for those who wait and put their trust in You. *(Refrain)*

Copyright © 1978 Damean Music. All Rights Reserved.

147   Star-Light

RON ELLIS

VERSE 1

1. A man and wom-an trav-eled far to Beth-le-

1. hem, led by a star. No room they found,

Copyright © 1979 by Raven Music. All Rights Reserved. Used with permission.

1. no one to care, 'til they came to a sta-ble bare

1. This fam-i-ly would ful-fill

1. prom-ise of ag - es, the Lord God's will. Shep-herds

1. came; an - gels sang: Peace on earth

1. to you all, you are loved.

REFRAIN

Star - light, star - bright, lead us on

through the dark - ness. Star - light, we

share you to-night. Bring us home in your light.

VERSE 2

2. God is here, Em-ma - nu - el.

2. Je - sus Christ, You are our Lord, Prince of Peace,

2. light from a- bove. Praise the Fa - ther, Son and

2. Spi - rit of love.

185

148 Suffering Servant Song

Words adapted by ROGER SMITH
Based on Isaiah 52:13; 53:12ff.

JAMES CHAUMONT

REFRAIN

We had all gone a-stray like sheep.

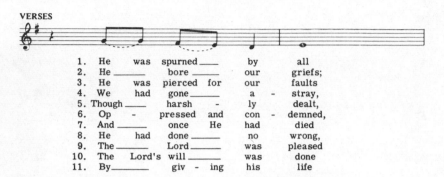

VERSES

1. He was spurned by all
2. He bore our griefs;
3. He was pierced for our faults
4. We had gone a - stray,
5. Though harsh - ly dealt,
6. Op - pressed and con - demned,
7. And once He had died
8. He had done no wrong,
9. The Lord was pleased
10. The Lord's will was done
11. By giv - ing his life

1. and a - void - ed by men,
2. he car - ried our pain,
3. and crushed for our sins.
4. each to our own way,
5. he o - pened not his mouth.
6. he was tak - en a - way.
7. for his peo - ple's sins,
8. nor spo - ken false,
9. to crush him in pain.
10. through this ser - vant of God.
11. and bear - ing our guilt,

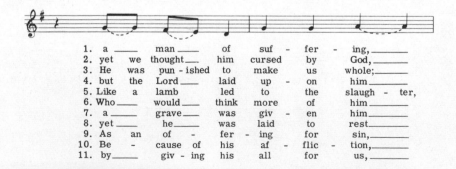

1. a man of suf - fer - ing,
2. yet we thought him cursed by God,
3. He was pun - ished to make us whole;
4. but the Lord laid up - on him
5. Like a lamb led to the slaugh - ter,
6. Who would think more of him
7. a grave was giv - en him
8. yet he was laid to rest
9. As an of - fer - ing for sin,
10. Be - cause of his af - flic - tion,
11. by giv - ing his all for us,

Copyright © 1975 by North American Liturgy Resources, Phoenix, Arizona 85029. All Rights Reserved.

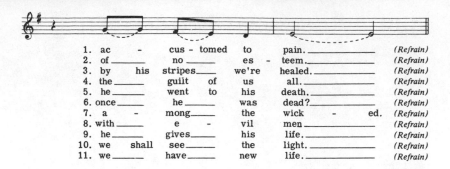

1. ac - cus - tomed to pain._____ (Refrain)
2. of_____ no_____ es - teem._____ (Refrain)
3. by his stripes_____ we're healed._____ (Refrain)
4. the_____ guilt of us all._____ (Refrain)
5. he_____ went to his death._____ (Refrain)
6. once_____ he_____ was dead?_____ (Refrain)
7. a - mong_____ the wick - ed._____ (Refrain)
8. with_____ e - vil men._____ (Refrain)
9. he_____ gives_____ his life._____ (Refrain)
10. we shall see_____ the light._____ (Refrain)
11. we_____ have_____ new life._____ (Refrain)

There's a Time, There's a Moment   149

MICHAEL B. LYNCH

REFRAIN

There's a time, there's a mo-ment.___ There's a
place, there's a cer-tain___ one that we will
find when we try.___ There's a
time, there's a mo-ment,___ ev-'ry time ev-'ry
mo-ment___ of our lives,___ ev-'ry
time, ev-'ry mo-ment of our lives.

VERSES

1. With ev - 'ry day we find Him stand - ing
2. His Spir - it fills the hearts of all who
3. Where two or more are gath - ered in His

1. by._____ Through ev - 'ry one we meet, He's
2. love._____ It reach - es out, em - brac - ing
3. name._____ The pres - ence of His love is

Copyright © 1969 by Michael B. Lynch. First published 1973 by Raven Music. All Rights Reserved.

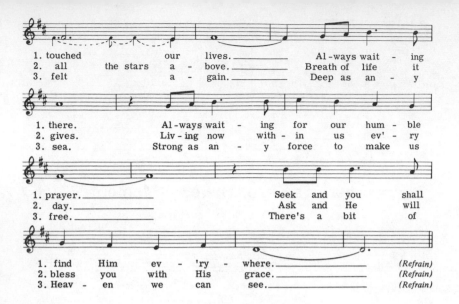

1. touched our lives.————— Al-ways wait - ing
2. all the stars a - bove.————— Breath of life it
3. felt a - gain.————— Deep as an - y

1. there. Al-ways wait - ing for our hum - ble
2. gives. Liv - ing now with - in us ev' - ry
3. sea. Strong as an - y force to make us

1. prayer.————— Seek and you shall
2. day.————— Ask and He will
3. free.————— There's a bit of

1. find Him ev - 'ry - where.————— *(Refrain)*
2. bless you with His grace.————— *(Refrain)*
3. Heav - en we can see.————— *(Refrain)*

150   This Is My Body

Based on 1 Corinthians 11:24,25

JOHN FOLEY, S.J.

VERSES

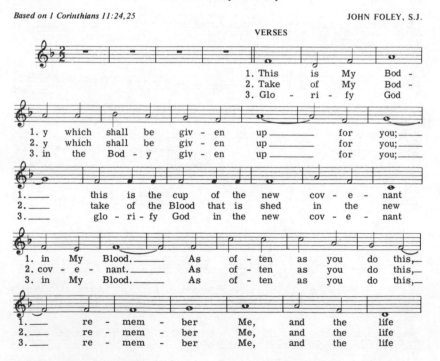

1. This is My Bod -
2. Take of My Bod -
3. Glo - ri - fy God

1. y which shall be giv - en up————— for you;—
2. y which shall be giv - en up————— for you;—
3. in the Bod - y giv - en up————— for you;—

1.— this is the cup of the new cov - e - nant
2.— take of the Blood that is shed in the new
3.— glo - ri - fy God in the new cov - e - nant

1. in My Blood.————— As of - ten as you do this,—
2. cov - e - nant.————— As of - ten as you do this,—
3. in My Blood.————— As of - ten as you do this,—

1.— re - mem - ber Me, and the life
2.— re - mem - ber Me, and the life
3.— re - mem - ber Me, and the life

Copyright © 1970 by John B. Foley, S.J.
Published exclusively by North American Liturgy Resources, Phoenix, Arizona 85029. All Rights Reserved.

1. that I give to the world._____
2. that I give to the world._____
3. that I give to the world._____

Trust in the Lord

151

Based on Isaiah 40:28-31

ROC O'CONNOR, S.J.

ANTIPHON

Trust in the Lord; you shall not tire._____

Serve you the Lord; you shall not weak-en. _____ For the Lord's own

strength_ will up-hold you.____ You shall re-new your life and

1. live._____ (Verse 1) 2.3. live._____ (Verse 2) Last live._____
(Verse 3)

VERSE 1

1. The Lord is our e-ter-nal God. He nei-ther faints____

1. nor grows wea-ry. Our hearts___ He probes from a-

1. far,____ know-ing our ways,____ know-ing our ways. ____ *(Antiphon)*

VERSE 2

2. Young hearts___ may grow faint and weak. Youths may col-lapse,____

2. ___ stum-ble and fall.____ They that hope in the Lord will re-

2. new their cour-age. They'll soar____ with ea-gle's might.___ *(Antiphon)*

Copyright © 1976 by Robert F. O'Connor, S.J. and North American Liturgy Resources, Phoenix, Arizona 85029. All Rights Reserved.

VERSE 3

3. Old men___ shall dream new dreams.___ Young men will find___

3. ___ wis-dom in vi-sions.___ The Lord will speak in our

3. life-time,___ show His face___ to those_ who wait.___ *(Antiphon)*

152   Valleys of Green

Based on Psalm 23

DAN SCHUTTE, S.J.

ANTIPHON

The Lord He will be my shep-herd;___ no-thing

more shall I want.___ He leads me a - long the

path of right ___ ac - cord - ing to His word.

VERSE 1

1. The Lord He will be my shep-herd;___ no - thing

1. more shall I want.___ In val - leys of green He

1. lets me lie;___ to rest - ful wa-ters He leads me.___*(Antiphon)*

VERSE 2

2. If ev - er I walk in dark-ness,___ noth - ing

2. more would I fear;___ There at my side You will

Copyright © 1971 by Daniel L. Schutte, S.J.
Published exclusively by North American Liturgy Resources, Phoenix, Arizona 85029. All Rights Reserved.

2. stand.____ Your staff will give me cour - age.____ *(Antiphon)*

VERSE 3

3. A ban - quet You set be - fore me,____ un - der the

3. eyes of my foes.____ And o - ver my head You

3. pour Your oil;____ my cup is flow - ing o - ver.____ *(Antiphon)*

VERSE 4

4. Your love will be al - ways with me____ ev - 'ry

4. day of my life.____ My home will be in

4. Yah - weh's house____ as long as I shall live.____ *(Antiphon)*

Wake From Your Sleep   153

DAN SCHUTTE, S.J.

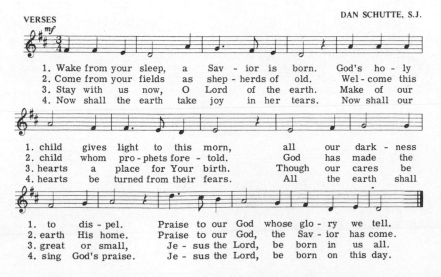

VERSES

1. Wake from your sleep, a Sav - ior is born. God's ho - ly
2. Come from your fields as shep - herds of old. Wel - come this
3. Stay with us now, O Lord of the earth. Make of our
4. Now shall the earth take joy in her tears. Now shall our

1. child gives light to this morn, all our dark - ness
2. child whom pro - phets fore - told. God has made the
3. hearts a place for Your birth. Though our cares be
4. hearts be turned from their fears. All the earth shall

1. to dis - pel. Praise to our God whose glo - ry we tell.
2. earth His home. Praise to our God, the Sav - ior has come.
3. great or small, Je - sus the Lord, be born in us all.
4. sing God's praise. Je - sus the Lord, be born on this day.

Copyright © 1977 by Daniel L. Schutte, S.J. and North American Liturgy Resources, Phoenix, Arizona 85029. All Rights Reserved.

154   We Praise You

MIKE BALHOFF

DARRYL DUCOTE
GARY DAIGLE

We praise You, O Lord, for all Your works are won-der-ful.

We praise You, O Lord, for-ev-er is Your love.

VERSES

1. Your wis-dom made the heav-ens and the earth, O Lord;
2. ⅞ You have cho-sen Ja-cob for Your-self, O Lord;
3. You led us out of Eg-ypt with a guid-ing hand.
4. The na-tions fash-ion sil-ver i-dols gold-en gods;
5. O House of Is-ra-el, now come to bless the Lord,

For weddings and family celebrations:

6. Hap-py is the home of you that fear the Lord;
7. ⅞ May the Lord give you His bles-sings all your days.

1. You formed the land then set the lights; and
2. so ten-der-ly You spoke His name; then
3. You raised Your arm to set us free. And
4. but none have hear-ing, speech or sight. Their
5. O House of Aar-on, bless His name. O

6. so fruit-ful shall your love be-come. Your
7. ⅞ May you see Him fill your land un-

1. like your love the sun will rule the day, and
2. called a ho-ly na-tion, Is-ra-el, to
3. like a ten-der vine You plan-ted us to
4. mak-ers shall be like their emp-ty gods, the
5. bless the Lord, all you who hon-or Him, and

6. child-ren flour-ish like the ol-ive plants, for-
7. til your child-ren bring their child-ren home to

1. stars will grace the night.   *(Refrain)*
2. make them Yours, You came.   *(Refrain)*
3. grow un-to the sea.   *(Refrain)*
4. Lord a-lone brings life.   *(Refrain)*
5. praise His ho-ly name.   *(Refrain)*

6. ev-er are you one.   *(Refrain)*
7. show His love a-gain.   *(Refrain)*

Copyright © 1978 Damean Music. All Rights Reserved.

What You Hear in the Dark

Based on Matthew 10:26,27; 5:13,14

DAN SCHUTTE, S.J.

ANTIPHON

What you hear in the dark

you must speak in the light.

You are salt for the earth;

you are light for the world._____

VERSES

1. Let your light be seen;_____ stand a-
2. Earth shall pass a - way;_____ heav - en will
3. God will keep you safe;_____ see the
4. Streng - then wea - ry arms;_____ stead-y all

1. gainst the night._____ Let your words of
2. be un - done._____ Nev - er shall the
3. spar-rows that fly._____ You are worth a
4. trem - ling knees._____ Say to ev - 'ry

1. mer - cy tell the glo-ry_____ of the Lord.
2. word of God be bro - ken_____ or des - troyed.
3. world of spar - rows shel - tered_____ by the Lord.
4. fear - ful heart: have cour-age,_____ trust in God.

Copyright © 1975 by Daniel L. Schutte, S.J. and North American Liturgy Resources, Phoenix, Arizona 85029. All Rights Reserved.

156

When You Seek Me

Jeremiah 29:11-14; 31:3,13

REV. CAREY LANDRY

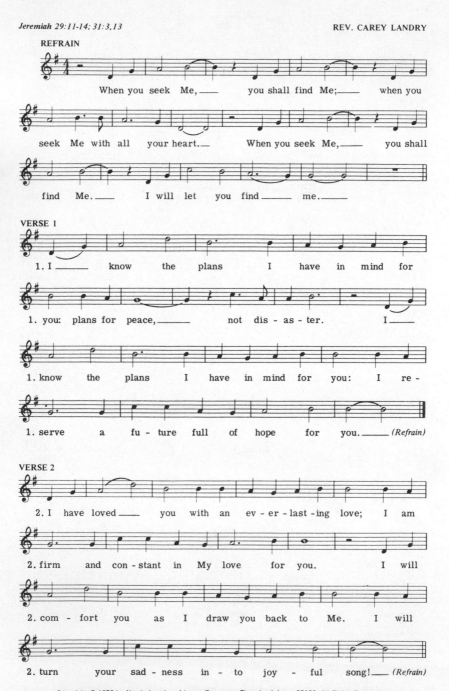

REFRAIN

When you seek Me, ___ you shall find Me; ___ when you seek Me with all your heart. ___ When you seek Me, ___ you shall find Me. ___ I will let you find ___ me.

VERSE 1

1. I ___ know the plans I have in mind for you: plans for peace, ___ not dis - as - ter. I ___ know the plans I have in mind for you: I re - serve a fu - ture full of hope for you. ___ *(Refrain)*

VERSE 2

2. I have loved ___ you with an ev - er - last - ing love; I am firm and con - stant in My love for you. I will com - fort you as I draw you back to Me. I will turn your sad - ness in - to joy - ful song! ___ *(Refrain)*

Copyright © 1979 by North American Liturgy Resources, Phoenix, Arizona 85029. All Rights Reserved.

With All My Heart

157

Luke 2:1-20,24
Revelation 2:28; 19:1-10; 21:16

RON ELLIS

Introduction

What shall I give to my Lord? What shall I
give to Him___ for all He's giv - en me?___
This is my song___ of joy.___

VERSES

*1. On this day is born our Sav-ior; (b) Je-sus Christ the light of na-tions.
**2. On this day the Lord is ris-en. Free us from our sins for-ev-er,
3. Praise our God who comes to save us. Great and small we sing His prais-es.
4. Then I heard the peo-ple sing-ing,"The reign of God is now for-ev-er."
5. Giv-ing thanks to God our Fa-ther, in His Son and Spir-it with us.

REFRAIN

A-men. Al - le-lu-ia.___ A-men. Al - le-lu-ia.___
A - men. Al - le - lu - ia.___

Copyright © 1977 by Raven Music. All Rights Reserved.

Without Clouds

158

DARRYL DUCOTE

REFRAIN

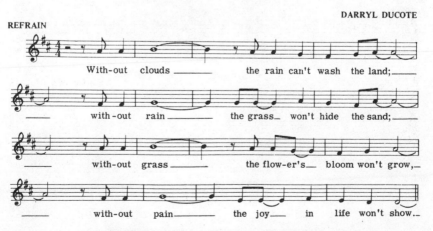

With-out clouds___ the rain can't wash the land;___
___ with-out rain___ the grass_ won't hide the sand;___
___ with-out grass___ the flow-er's_ bloom won't grow,___
___ with-out pain___ the joy___ in life won't show.___

Copyright © 1971, 1979 by Damean Music. All Rights Reserved.

195

1. Nev-er saw a sun - rise that did - n't
2. I'm not a - fraid of pain or threats it
3. There's one Who knew our pain. There's one Who

1. fol - low night; hard-ly saw it shin-ing till a shad - ow
2. seems to give, though it on - ly tears at life, with lit - tle
3. felt our loss and yet He knew a love that went be -

1. blocked its light; nev - er took a jour - ney
2. left to live. Still it won't con - quer me
3. yond the cost. He dared to lose it all

1. and not leave some place be - hind, not feel some
2. if I can learn to bend; for when its
3. to trust the Fath - er's care, and God re -

1. an - guish be - fore some peace of mind. *(Refrain)*
2. course is run, re - newed, I'll rise a - gain. *(Refrain)*
3. stored His life and con - quered death's de - spair. *(Refrain)*

159   With What Great Love

Isaiah 53:2-5; 52:13

REV. CAREY LANDRY

VERSE 1

1. With-out beau-ty, with-out maj - es - ty we

1. saw Him; a thing des-pised and re jec-ted, a

1. man of sor-rows, fam-i - li-ar with pain. We took no ac - count of

1. Him. Yet ours were the suf-fer-ings He bore;

1. ours the sor - rows He car - ried. He was pierced and

Copyright © 1977 by North American Liturgy Resources, Phoenix, Arizona 85029. All Rights Reserved.

1. crushed__ for our sins,__ and through His wounds__ we are healed.__

REFRAIN

Oh, Je - sus,__ Je - sus, with what great love__ You have

loved us.__ Oh, Je - sus,__ Je - sus, with

1.
2.

what great love__ You love. *(Verse 2)* love.

VERSE 2

2. We are His tri-bute,__ we__ His heirs;__ He is the

2. ran-som that was paid.__ His soul's an-guish o-ver;__ He has seen the

2. light, and He shall have long life.__

2. He has been lift - ed up, ex - alt - ed.__ He has been

2. raised__ to great heights. Through Him the will__ of the

2. Fath -er has been done__ and we shall have long life.__ *(Refrain)*

The Word Who Is Life

160

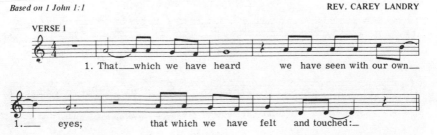

Based on 1 John 1:1

REV. CAREY LANDRY

VERSE 1

1. That__which we have heard we have seen with our own__

1.__ eyes; that which we have felt and touched:__

Copyright © 1975 by Rev. Carey Landry and North American Liturgy Resources, Phoenix, Arizona 85029. All Rights Reserved.

REFRAIN

The Word who is life,— the Word who is life,—

the Word who is life for us.

To Him be glo - ry, all hon-or and praise. To Him be

glo - ry : Je - sus, our Sav - ior and Lord.—

VERSES 2 and 3

2. He is the Light of lights— our Re -
3. He is the Bread of Life— Won - der,

1. deem - er King;— He is the Lord of lords:— *(Refrain)*
2. Coun - sel - lor;— He is the Prince of peace:— *(Refrain)*

161 You Are My Friends

Verses: Psalm 100
Refrain: John 15:12-15

DONALD J. REAGAN

REFRAIN

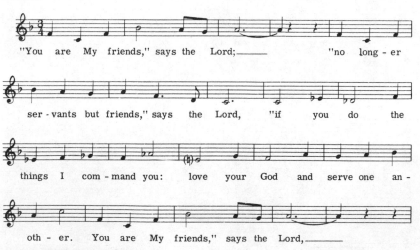

"You are My friends," says the Lord;— "no long - er

ser - vants but friends," says the Lord, "if you do the

things I com - mand you: love your God and serve one an -

oth - er. You are My friends," says the Lord,—

Copyright © 1979 by North American Liturgy Resources, Phoenix, Arizona 85029. All Rights Reserved.

"no long - er ser - vants___ but friends."___

VERSE 1

1. Re joice! Sing to the Lord.___ Serve Him with

1. glad -ness of heart.___ Come be - fore Him with

1. joy - ful song. Raise your voice to the Lord.___ *(Refrain)*

VERSE 2

2. Know that the Lord is our God.___ We are the

2. flock that He tends.___ Come be - fore Him with

2. thanks and praise. Raise your voice to the Lord.___ *(Refrain)*

VERSE 3

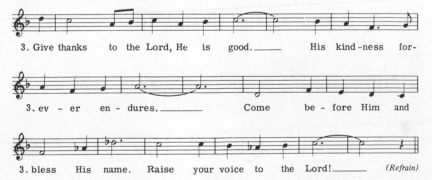

3. Give thanks to the Lord, He is good.___ His kind -ness for-

3. ev - er en - dures.___ Come be - fore Him and

3. bless His name. Raise your voice to the Lord!___ *(Refrain)*

199

162

Melchizedek Alleluia

ROGER SMITH

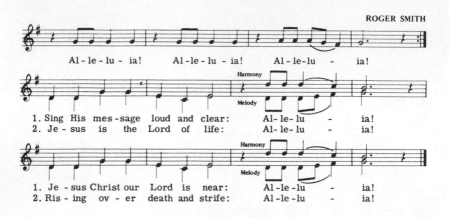

Al - le - lu - ia! Al - le - lu - ia! Al - le - lu - ia!

Harmony

Melody

1. Sing His mes - sage loud and clear: Al - le - lu - ia!
2. Je - sus is the Lord of life: Al - le - lu - ia!

Harmony

Melody

1. Je - sus Christ our Lord is near: Al - le - lu - ia!
2. Ris - ing ov - er death and strife: Al - le - lu - ia!

Copyright © 1975 by North American Liturgy Resources, Phoenix, Arizona 85029. All Rights Reserved.

163

Alleluia

DONALD J. REAGAN

ANTIPHON

Al - le - lu - ia, al - le - lu - ia, al - le - lu - ia!

VERSE

Speak to me, O— Lord;— Your ser - vant is list - en - ing.

You have the words of ev - er - last - ing life.—

Round

Al - le - lu - ia, al - le - lu - ia, al - le - lu - ia

Copyright © 1979 by North American Liturgy Resources, Phoenix, Arizona 85029. All Rights Reserved.

Lenten Gospel Acclamation 164

JOE REGAN

REFRAIN

Glo - ry and praise to You, O Lord Je-sus Christ.____

VERSE

We have stilled our hearts and now we lis-ten to Your word.____

Copyright © 1975 by North American Liturgy Resources, Phoenix, Arizona 85029. All Rights Reserved.

Praise to You, Jesus Christ 165

(Gospel Procession and Acclamation)

DONALD J. REAGAN

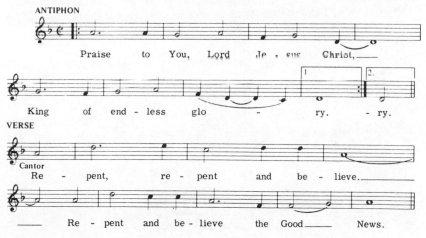

ANTIPHON

Praise to You, Lord Je - sus Christ,____

King of end - less glo - ry. - ry.

VERSE

Cantor

Re - pent, re - pent and be - lieve.____

____ Re - pent and be - lieve the Good____ News.

ANTIPHON

Praise to You, Lord Je - sus Christ,____

King of end - less glo - ry.

Copyright © 1979 by North American Liturgy Resources, Phoenix, Arizona 85029. All Rights Reserved.

166 We Believe

REV. CAREY LANDRY

VERSES 1, 2 and 4

1. We be-lieve in___ God the Fa——ther, We be-
2. We be-lieve in___ Je-sus Christ, the Lord. We be-
4. We be-lieve in the Ho-ly Spi——rit. We be-

1. lieve, we be-lieve. We be-lieve He___ is the
2. lieve, we be-lieve. We be-lieve He___ is God's
4. lieve, we be-lieve. We be-lieve in the Ho-ly

1. Ho—ly One. We be-lieve, we be-lieve. *(Verse 2)*
2. on—ly Son. We be-lieve, we be-lieve. *(Verse 3)*
4. Church of God. We be-lieve, we be-lieve. *(Verse 5)*

VERSES 3 and 5

3. He was con-ceived by the Ho—ly Spi—rit;
5. We be-lieve in God's for-give—ness;___ the

3. born of the Vir-gin Ma——ry; For___ us He died and was
5. re-sur-rec-tion from the dead. We be-lieve in life ev-er-

Last time to *CODA*

3. bur—ied. On the third day He rose a—gain.___ *(Verse 4)*
5. last—ing. We be-

CODA

lieve,___ we be-lieve. A—men. We be-

lieve. A—men. We be-lieve.___

Copyright © 1979 by North American Liturgy Resources, Phoenix, Arizona 85029. All Rights Reserved.

Holy

JOHN FOLEY, S.J.

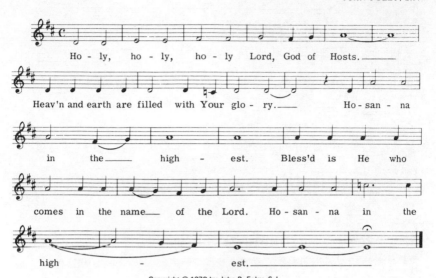

Ho - ly, ho - ly, ho - ly Lord, God of Hosts.

Heav'n and earth are filled with Your glo - ry. Ho - san - na

in the high - est. Bless'd is He who

comes in the name of the Lord. Ho - san - na in the

high - est.

Copyright © 1979 by John B. Foley, S.J.
Published exclusively by North American Liturgy Resources, Phoenix, Arizona 85029. All Rights Reserved.

Hosanna for Joy

ROGER SMITH

REFRAIN

Ho - san - na, ho - san - na in the

1.3.5.7.   2.4.6.   Last

high - est. est. *(Verse)* est.

VERSE 1

1. Ho - ly, ho - ly ho - ly Lord. God of pow-er and might.

VERSE 2

2. Heav - en and earth are full of your glo - ry.

VERSE 3

3. Bless - ed is he who comes in the name of the Lord.

Copyright © 1975 by North American Liturgy Resources, Phoenix, Arizona 85029. All Rights Reserved.

169 Anamnesis I

TOM CONRY

VERSE

You are here and You are com-ing still though You have died and ris-en. You are liv-ing for all time. We re-mem-ber and we call You here a-mong us now.

Copyright © 1978 by North American Liturgy Resources, Phoenix, Arizona 85029. All Rights Reserved.

170 Anamnesis II

TOM CONRY

When we eat this bread, when we drink this cup, we pro-claim Your glo-ry un-til You come a-gain.

Copyright © 1978 by North American Liturgy Resources, Phoenix, Arizona 85029. All Rights Reserved.

171 Amen

TOM CONRY

A-men, a-men. As You say, so let it be. All Your peo-ple You set free. Free to stand, free to start, let it

Copyright © 1978 by North American Liturgy Resources, Phoenix, Arizona 85029. All Rights Reserved.

Acclamations

REV. CAREY LANDRY

Copyright © 1979 by North American Liturgy Resources, Phoenix, Arizona 85029. All Rights Reserved.
Text copyright © 1975 by I.C.E.L. All Rights Reserved. Used with permission.

173   Mass in A Minor

JOE ZSIGRAY

Ⓐ Lord, Have Mercy

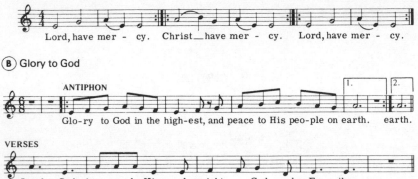

Lord, have mer - cy. Christ — have mer - cy. Lord, have mer - cy.

Ⓑ Glory to God

ANTIPHON

Glo-ry to God in the high-est, and peace to His peo-ple on earth.   earth.

VERSES

1. Lord God, heav-en-ly King, al-might-y God and Fa-ther.

2. We wor-ship You, we give You thanks, we praise You for Your glo-ry.

3. Lord Je-sus Christ, on-ly Son of the Fa-ther, Lord God, Lamb of God;

4. You take a-way — the sins of the world; — have mer-cy on us.

4. You are seat-ed at the right hand of the Fa-ther; re-ceive — our prayer.

5. For You a-lone are the Ho-ly One; You a-lone are the

5. Lord. You a-lone are most — high, Je-sus Christ, with the Ho-ly

5. Spir - it in the glo-ry of God the Fa-ther.

6. A - men, a - men, a - men.

Ⓒ Alleluia

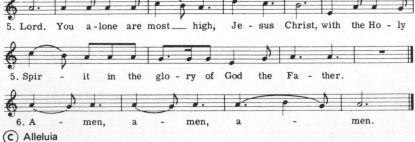

Al-le-lu-ia, al-le-lu-ia, al-le-lu-ia. —

Copyright © 1978 by North American Liturgy Resources, Phoenix, Arizona 85029. All Rights Reserved.

D General Intercessions: Response

a cappella

O Lord, hear our prayer; grant us Your peace.

E Holy, Holy

(♩ = 96)

REFRAIN

1.
2.

Ho-san-na in the high-est,— ho-san-na in the high-est.— high-est.—

VERSES

1. Ho - ly, ho - ly, ho - ly Lord, God of pow'r and might.—

1. Heav - en and earth are full of Your glo - ry.

2. Bless - ed is He Who comes in the name of the Lord.

F Christ Has Died

(♩ – 96)

1.
2.

Christ has died, Christ has ris - en, Christ will come a - gain. gain.

G When We Eat This Bread

(♩ = 96)

When we eat this bread— and drink this cup, we pro-

1.
2.

claim Your death, Lord— Je -sus,— un-til You come in glo - ry.— - ry.

H Dying You Destroyed Our Death

(♩ = 96)

Dy - ing, You de - stroyed— our — death; ris - ing, You re-

1.
2.

stored— our— life; Lord Je - sus, come in glo - ry. glo - ry.

I Lord, by Your Cross

Lord, by Your cross and re-sur-rec - tion You have set us
free; You are the Sav - ior of the world.___
1. world.___ 2.

J Amen

A - men, a - men, a - men.___

K Our Father

Our___ Fa - ther,___ who art in heav-en, ___ hal-low'd__ be__ Thy
name.___ Thy king-dom come,___ Thy__ will be done___ on
earth as it is in heav - en.___ Give us this day our dai-ly bread,__
___ and for - give us our tres-pas-ses as we for-give those who
tres - pass a - gainst us.___ And lead us not in - to temp-
ta - tion,___ but de - liv - er us from e - vil.___

6

(Celebrant:) Deliver us, Lord from every evil, and grant us . . . Jesus Christ. For the king-dom, the
pow'r and the glo - ry are Yours, now and for - ev - er.

L Lamb of God

Lamb___ of God,___ You take a way the sins of the
1.2. world; have mer - cy on us. 3. world;___ grant___ us peace.

174 All the Ends of the Earth

BOB DUFFORD, S.J.

REFRAIN

All the ends of the earth, __ all you crea-tures of the sea, __ lift up your eyes to the won-ders of the Lord. __ For the Lord of the earth, __ the Mas-ter of the sea, __ has come with jus-tice for the world. __

VERSES 1 and 2:

1. Break in-to song at the deeds of the Lord, __ the
2. Heav-en and earth shall re-joice in His might; ev-'ry heart, __

Copyright©1981 by Robert J. Dufford, S.J., and NALR, 10802 N. 23rd Ave., Phoenix, Arizona 85029. All rights reserved.

won - ders He has __ done in ev - 'ry age. __
_____ ev - 'ry na - tion call Him

to REFRAIN

Lord. _____

VERSE 3:

3. The Lord has made His sal -

va - tion known, faith - ful to His

prom - is - es of old. _____

__ Let the ends of the earth, __

__ let the sea and all it

holds make mu - sic be -

to REFRAIN

fore our King! _____

175 Alleluia

MIKE BALHOFF
DARRYL DUCOTE
GARY DAIGLE

REFRAIN

Al - le - lu - ia, al - le - lu - ia,

al - le - lu - ia.

VERSES:

1. Give thanks to the Lord for

He is good, His mer - cy en - dures for-

ev - er. ____ Let the house of

Copyright©1981 by Damean Music. Published exclusively by NALR. 10802 N. 23rd Ave.,
Phoenix, Arizona 85029. All rights reserved.

Is - ra - el say His mer - cy en - dures for - ev - er.

to REFRAIN

Coda

This is the day _____ the Lord _____ has made, let us re - joice and be glad. _____

to REFRAIN

2. My strength and my courage is the Lord,
His mercy endures forever.
Let the cry of victory sound
His mercy endures forever.

3. The Lord's right hand has struck with pow'r,
His mercy endures forever.
I shall live and never die,
His mercy endures forever.

176 Alleluia, People of God

TEXT: Amos 4:12; Matthew 4:13-17.
USE: Celebration of the Word;
Gospel Acclamation.

LUCIEN DEISS

ANTIPHON *(Lower notes - Harmony)*

Al - le - lu - ia, Al - le -
lu - ia! Al- le - lu - ia! A -
men! Al-le - lu - ia!

VERSES:

1.- 3. Peo - ple of God, pre -
pare your - selves to meet the Lord, your God.

Copyright©1982 by Lucien Deiss. Published exclusively by NALR. 10802 N. 23rd Ave.,
Phoenix, Arizona 85029. All rights reserved.

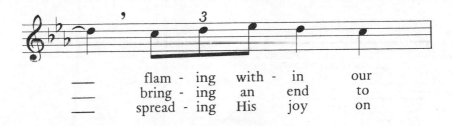

1. The Good News pro-claimed by
2. The Good News pro-claimed by
3. The Good News pro-claimed by

Je - sus is a burst of fire _____
Je - sus is a flash of light _____
Je - sus is a song of love _____

____ flam - ing with - in our
____ bring - ing an end to
____ spread - ing His joy on

(To Antiphon)

hearts, Al-le - lu - ia!
night, Al-le - lu - ia!
earth, Al-le - lu - ia!

177   Alleluia, Your Word

TEXT: John 8:12; Hebrews 4:12.
USE: Celebration of the Word of God;
       Gospel Acclamation.

LUCIEN DEISS

ANTIPHON *(Lower notes - Harmony)*

Al - le - lu - ia!   Al - le -
lu - ia!   Al- le - lu-ia!   Al- le-lu - ia!
Al - le -lu - ia, — Al - le - lu - ia!

VERSES:

1. Your —— Word, O — Lord, is the
2. Your —— Word, O — Lord, is the
3. Your —— Word, O — Lord, was made

light   of   the   world. ——
fire   which   con - sumes. ——
flesh   of   the   Vir - gin.

Copyright©1982 by Lucien Deiss. Published exclusively by NALR. 10002 N. 23rd Ave.,
Phoenix, Arizona 85029. All rights reserved.

Your ___ Word, O Lord, is the
Your ___ Word, O Lord, is a
Your ___ Word, O Lord, is Your
(To Antiphon)

dawn-ing light ___ of our night.
flash-ing sword ___ bring - ing truth.
ris - en Son: ___ He is Christ.

Answer When I Call   178

JOHN FOLEY, S.J.

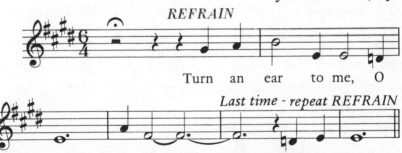

REFRAIN

Turn an ear to me, O

Last time - repeat REFRAIN

Lord; an-swer ___ when I call. ___

1. Like an owl in the desert,
   A sparrow, alone and astray,
   I watch, I wait.

2. Like the grass of the summer,
   Like shadows that wither and fade,
   O Lord, I wait.

3. Give an ear to my pleading,
   And hear me, O God of my heart;
   I wait, I pray.

Copyright©1981 by John B. Foley, S.J., and NALR, 10802 N. 23rd Ave.,
Phoenix, Arizona 85029. All rights reserved.

179   At All Times

♩ = 69   LUCIEN DEISS

ANTIPHON *(Lower notes - Harmony)*

But at all times, O Lord, _____ the

song of Your praise will sing on my lips.

But at all times, O Lord, _____

_____ Your joy will shine in my

heart, Flame of Glad-ness. _____

VERSES:

1. There is a time for giv - ing
2. There is a time for wound -
3. There is a time for weep -
4. There is a time to scat - ter
5. There is a time for search -
6. There is a time for tear -
7. There is a time for lov -

Copyright©1982 by Lucien Deiss. Published exclusively by NALR. 10802 N. 23rd Ave.,
Phoenix, Arizona 85029. All rights reserved.

birth; there is a time for dy -
ing; there is a time for heal -
ing; there is a time for laugh -
stones; there is a time to gath -
ing; there is a time for los -
ing; there is a time for sew -
ing; there is a time for hat -

ing. There is a time for
ing. There is a time for
ing There is a time for
er. There is a time for
ing. There is a time for
ing. There is a time for
ing. There is a time for

plant - ing, and there is a time to
tear - ing down, and there is a time for
mourn - ing and there is a time for
kiss - ing, and there is a time ___
keep - ing, and there is a time for
si - lence and there is a time for
mak - ing war, and there is a time for

(To Antiphon)

up - root the plant.
build - ing.
danc - ing.
to ___ re - frain.
throw - ing a - way.
speak - ing.
mak - ing peace.

180 Awake, O Sleeper

MIKE BALHOFF
DARRYL DUCOTE
GARY DAIGLE

REFRAIN

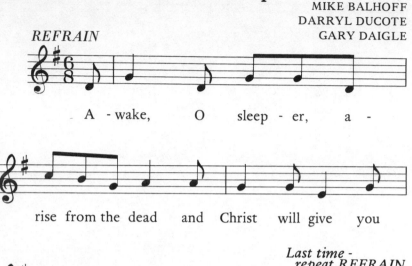

A - wake, O sleep - er, a -

rise from the dead and Christ will give you

Last time -
repeat REFRAIN

light,___ Christ will give you light.

VERSES:

1. Once you were lost___ in the

dark - ness. ___ Now you are

Copyright©1981 by Damean Music. Published exclusively by NALR. 10802 N. 23rd Ave.,
Phoenix, Arizona 85029. All rights reserved.

light in the Lord.

to REFRAIN

Live each day as chil - dren of light.

2. Light brings forth ev'ry goodness.
   Justice and truth are revealed.
   Seek the way that pleases the Lord.

3. I am the Light of the World.
   I came to make the sightless see.
   Follow Me and you will find life.

181 Awaken, My Heart

TEXT: Matthew 25:1-13, 40.
USE: Hymn for all times; Advent;
32nd Sunday, A.

LUCIEN DEISS

A - wak - en, my heart! A -
wak - en, my heart! Read - y your lamp with its
light, for the Lord soon will
come. A - wak - en, my heart!
Rise up and sing, and pre-pare your-self for the
feast of the King-dom!

Copyright © 1982 by Lucien Deiss. Published exclusively by NALR. 10802 N. 23rd Ave.,
Phoenix, Arizona 85029. All rights reserved.

1.-3. In the midst of the night comes a

cry ring-ing out: "Be-hold the Bride-groom comes!"

Omitted if instruments
are not used.

1. Do you not
2. Do you not
3. Do you not

re-cog-nize Me
re-cog-nize Me
re-cog-nize Me

(To Antiphon)

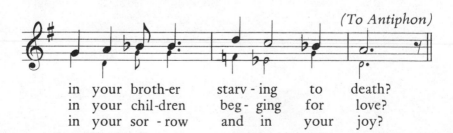

in your broth-er starv-ing to death?
in your chil-dren beg-ging for love?
in your sor-row and in your joy?

182 Beatitudes

Text:
MIKE BALHOFF

Music:
DARRYL DUCOTE

VERSES:

1. Blest are you, ___ the poor ___ who trust ___ the Fa - ther with your lives, ___ For with - in ___ your heart ___ is born ___ the King -dom of ___ the Lord. ___ Blest are you, ___ the sor - row-ing, ___ who know your Fa -ther wise ___ For with - in ___ your heart ___

Copyright © 1973 by Damean Music. Published exclusively by NALR. 10802 N. 23rd Ave., Phoenix, Arizona 85029. All rights reserved.

224

— is born — the King-dom of — the Lord. ———

REFRAIN

— Let your — light shine — for

all the world — to see: ——— The

bright-ness of — your life ——— with- in, — the

peace that set you free.——— Let your —

light shine ——————— to

fill your nights — and days; ———

All will see — the deeds — you do — and
give your Fa - ther praise. ____

2. Blest are you, the lowly ones,
   Who know your need to share,
   For within your heart is born
   The Kingdom of the Lord.

   Blest are you, whose searching souls
   Will draw you to God's care,
   For within your heart is born
   The Kingdom of the Lord.

3. Blest are those whose mercy shows
   The Father's love to all
   For within your heart is born
   The Kingdom of the Lord

   Blest are you, the pure in heart,
   Who live the Father's call,
   For within your heart is born
   The Kingdom of the Lord

4. Blest are you who work for peace
   Among the Father's own,
   For within your heart is born
   The Kingdom of the Lord

   Blest are you who suffer hate
   To prepare the day to come,
   For within your heart is born
   The Kingdom of the Lord.

Beginning Today

183

Text:
MIKE BALHOFF

Music:
DARRYL DUCOTE

REFRAIN

Be - gin-ning to-day_ my morn-ings are Yours,_ the hopes that dawn_ in their light. Be - gin-ning to day _ my eve-nings and dreams,_ my gift to you _ is my life._____

VERSES:

1. I will al - ways re-mem - ber the time _ ___ You first called ___ me

Copyright © 1973 by Damean Music. Published exclusively by NALR. 10802 N. 23rd Ave., Phoenix, Arizona 85029. All rights reserved.

out of my emp - ty sleep ____

____ to wak - en in me ____ the hope ____

____ of a new ____ day, the

to REFRAIN

love I want - ed to seek. Be -

2. You gave me Your life, Lord, as sign of the springtime
   Beginning in me each day.
   You made me a child with wonder and love, Lord,
   To newly discover Your way.

3. You are the Lord who forgave all my failings
   And lovingly called me to try.
   You are the rainfall that offered the seedling.
   The chance to grow to the sky.

4. I promise this day I will sing for the world
   The song we begin to share,
   To fill up tomorrow with sounds of our love, Lord,
   The hopes and dreams that we bear.

Bless, O Lord, Your People 184

JOE PINSON

REFRAIN

Bless, O Lord, Your peo-ple; hear us

as we sing and pray. Bless, O Lord, Your

peo-ple, and guide us in Your way.

VERSES:

1. Bless the rich, and bless the poor.
2. Bless the young, and bless the old.
3. Bless the church, and bless the Word.

Bless the fast and the slow. Bless the black, and
Bless the good and the kind. Bless the wo-man
Bless the weak and the strong. Bless the pas-tor

to REFRAIN

bless the white. Bless all rac-es here be-low.
and the man. Bless each heart and soul and mind.
and the priest. Bless all those who sing this song.

Copyright © 1981 by NALR. 10802 N. 23rd Ave., Phoenix, Arizona 85029.
All rights reserved.

185 The Bread of Rejoicing

USE: Eucharist; Communion; Corpus Christi.

♩ = 92

LUCIEN DEISS

ANTIPHON (*Lower notes - Harmony*)

To be - come the bread of re - joic - ing, to be - come the wine of Your love, to be - come __ the song of Your glad - ness, to be - come Your bod-y, O Lord __ Je - sus Christ!

VERSES:

1. See, O Lord, the bread of our pain, the
2. See, O Lord, the bread of our toil, the
3. See, O Lord, the bread of our love, the
4. See, O Lord, the bread of our life, the
5. See, O Lord, the wine of our joy, the

Copyright © 1982 by Lucien Deiss. Published exclusively by NALR. 10802 N. 23rd Ave., Phoenix, Arizona 85029. All rights reserved.

bread   we   knead   with   our
bread   we   sow   which   is
bread   we   break   and   we
bread   of   heav - en   which
wine   which   flows   from   the

hands worn by sor - row,   the bread of our
ripe now for har - vest,   the bread of our
share with each oth - er,   the hearts that we
bright - ens our path-way,   the bread of the
grapes of our vine-yards,   the joy of the

grief, the bread of our suf - f'ring.
work, the bread of our la - bor.
give bring joy to the lone - ly. } 1.-5. Give
way that leads to the King - dom.
earth, the wine of the feast - ing.

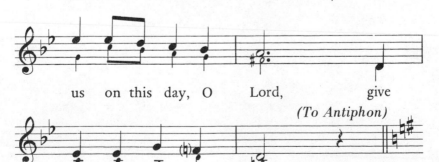

us   on this day, O   Lord,   give

(To Antiphon)

us   our   dai - ly   bread.

186 By Name I Have Called You

CAREY LANDRY

Be still...be still...and know that I am your God.
Be still...be still...and know that I am with you. *(Refrain)*

REFRAIN

By name I have called you, by
name I will save you, by name you are
Mine, you are pre - cious — to Me; by
name I have called you, by
name I will send you, ——— for -
ev - er, with you I will be.

Copyright © 1980 by NAI R. 10802 N. 23rd Ave., Phoenix, Arizona 85029.
All rights reserved.

1. Be - fore you were born I knew you; _____ with - in your mo - ther's womb I formed you; _____ I ap - point - ed you to

2. Com - fort, com - fort my peo - ple; _____ speak to their hearts; _____ speak ten - der - ly,

1.

to REFRAIN

1. speak in My name. _____

2.

to REFRAIN

2. ten - der - ly to them. _____

187 City of God

DAN SCHUTTE, S.J.

VERSES 1 and 2:

1. A - wake from your slum-ber! _
2. We are sons of the morn-ing; _

A - rise from your sleep!
we are daugh - ters of day.

A new day is dawn - ing __
The One Who has loved us __

for all those who weep.
has bright- ened our way.

The peo - ple in dark-ness __
The Lord of all kind-ness __

have seen a great light.
has called us to be

Copyright©1981 by Daniel L. Schutte, S.J., and NALR, 10802 N. 23rd Ave.,
Phoenix, Arizona 85029. All rights reserved.

The Lord of our long-ing ___
a light for His peo-ple ___

to REFRAIN

has con-quered the night. ___
to set their hearts free. ___

REFRAIN

Let us build the cit-y ___ of

God. May our tears be

turned in-to danc - ing! For the

Lord, our Light and our Love, ___ has

turned ___ the night in-to day!

3. God _____ is light; _____
_ in Him there is no
dark - ness. Let us walk _____
_ in His light, _____ His
chil - dren, one and all. _____

O com- fort My peo - ple; ___
make gen- tle your words. Pro-claim to My

236

cit - y _____ the day of her

to REFRAIN

birth. _____

VERSE 4:

4. O cit - y ___ of glad-ness, ___

now lift up your voice! Pro -claim the good

tid - ings ___ that all may re -

to REFRAIN

joice! _____

237

188 Clothed in the Lord's Love

CAREY LANDRY

Copyright ©1980 by NALR 10802 N. 23rd Ave., Phoenix, Arizona 85029.
All rights reserved.

VERSE 1:

1. Who can dis - cern love _____ but the

one who is the be - lov - ed? ___

How could I've learned to love the Lord had

to REFRAIN

He not loved me from the first? ____

VERSE 2:

2. I love my be-lov - ed to - tal - ly, where He

is there am I as well; ___ no

strang-er to Him am I; ___ u - nit- ed to Him am

I; _____ the lov - er has found ____

to REFRAIN

_____ the Be - lov - ed. _____

189 Come, My Children

MIKE BALHOFF
DARRYL DUCOTE
GARY DAIGLE

VERSES 1, 2, and 4:

1. I will bless the Lord at all times. His
praise shall be ev - er on my lips. Let my
soul glo - ry in the Lord, the *to REFRAIN*
low - ly will hear me and be glad.

REFRAIN

Come, come my chil - dren, I will
teach you how great is the
Lord.

Copyright © 1981 by Damean Music. Published exclusively by NALR. 10802 N. 23rd Ave., Phoenix, Arizona 85029. All rights reserved.

2. Glorify the Lord with me.
   Let us together praise His name.
   In my need He has answered me,
   Delivering me from all my fears.

4. I will turn from sin to do Your will.
   Seek peace and follow in its way,
   For the Lord raises up the lives
   Of the just who cry out to Him.

VERSE 3:

3. Taste   and   see   the

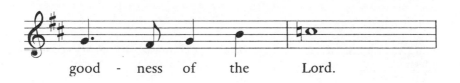

good - ness   of   the   Lord.

Hap - py are they who take   ref - uge in

(D.C.)
to VERSE 4

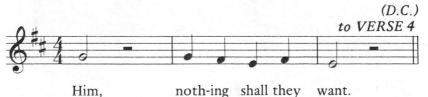

Him,   noth-ing shall they want.

190 The Dawn of Day

TEXT: Revelation 21:1-5; 22:20.
USE: Celebration of Sunday, the day of the Lord.
Fifth Sunday of Easter, C.

LUCIEN DEISS

♩ = 112 *(Lower notes - Harmony)*

1. For soon the dawn of
2. For soon the an - gels'
3. For soon your pain will
4. For soon Your King - dom

day will come and the
choir will sing and the
dis - ap - pear and the
will be here and Your

light will burst forth in your
por - tals of heav'n o - pen
wound in your heart will be
love will a - bide in our

night. _____ For soon the dawn of
wide. _____ For soon the an - gels'
healed. _____ For soon your pain will
lives. _____ For soon Your King - dom

day will come and the
choir will sing and the
dis - ap - pear and the
will be here and the

Copyright © 1982 by Lucien Deiss. Published exclusively by NALR. 10802 N. 23rd Ave., Phoenix, Arizona 85029. All rights reserved.

love   in   your   heart   will   re -
glo - ry   of   Christ   will   ap -
Lord   will   take   you   in   His
bright - ness   of   Christ   will   be

joice.__   On this   day   of the   Lord,   on this
pear.__   On this   day,   earth and heav'n   will be
arms.__   No more   death,   no more tears,   no more
seen.__   On this   day   with-out   end,   gath-ered

day   of   our   joy,   peace   and
joined   in   Your   love,   and   the
grief,   no   more   pain,   for   the
all   in   Your   home,   face   to

beau - ty   will   fill __   the   earth.__
feast - ing   will   nev - er   end.__   1.-4. For
old world will   pass __   a - way.__
face   we   will   see __   You,   Lord.__

soon,_   O Lord,_ Your   day __ will come.   Yes,

soon,   O   Lord Je - sus   Christ. __

191 For Everything There Is a Time

DONALD J. REAGAN

REFRAIN

There is a time for ev-'ry-thing be-neath the heav-ens; ____ there is a sea-son fit-ting for each part of life. All things, God ___ has free-ly giv-en in His love, ____ for use and bless-ing, each in its ap-point-ed time. ____

Copyright © 1981 by NALR. 10802 N. 23rd Ave., Phoenix, Arizona 85029.
All rights reserved.

1. There's a time to weep and a time to laugh,
   A time to mourn and a time to dance,
   A time to gather and a time to scatter,
   A time to plant and a time to harvest;
   So take each day and live it as a precious gift;
   For ev'rything in life there is a time.

2. There's a time to find and a time to lose,
   A time to tear and a time to repair,
   A time to be silent and a time to speak,
   A time to be born and a time to die.
   A thousand years are but a moment in His sight;
   What is now, has already been, what will be, now already is,
   So take each day and live it as a precious gift;
   For ev'rything in life, there is a time.

Gifts for Our Lord   192

SHELDON COHEN

Gifts for our Lord we bring to You now; with bread and with wine we will come. As in days long a- go when Your words You did sow, we will

Copyright ©1981 by NALR. 10802 N. 23rd Ave., Phoenix, Arizona 85029.
All rights reserved.

reap the har - vest of love. _____

Gifts for our Lord we bring to You

now, our hearts ev - er o - pened to

You. _____ We will share with all

men, we will see You a - gain in the
(friends,)

eyes of all who be - lieve. _____

_____ With You by our side, Your

love ev - er - last - ing, with You, Je - sus,

Lord, we will start life a - new.

Gifts for our Lord we bring to You

now, Your life giv - en free - ly for

all. _____ Let us shed no more

tears, as we end all our fears, hold-ing

hands and shar - ing Your love. _____

193 Give Us Living Water

MIKE BALHOFF
DARRYL DUCOTE
GARY DAIGLE

REFRAIN

Give us liv - ing wa - ter,

we ask you, O Lord, that we ne - ver

thirst _____ a - gain.

VERSES 1 and 2:

1. Leav - ing E - gypt we
2. Who - ev - er drinks _____ the

cried _____ in our thirst,
wa - ter from the earth

give us wa - ter to drink.
will feel thirst _____ once more.

Copyright 1981 by Damean Music. Published exclusively by NALR. 10802 N. 23rd Ave., Phoenix, Arizona 85029. All rights reserved.

We — quar - reled and
But if you drink — the

test - ed our God, say -ing, "Is — the Lord
wa - ter I give you will nev-er — be

to REFRAIN

with us or not?"_____
thirs - ty a - gain._____

VERSE 3:

3. The wa - ter I give to

you shall be - come a

┌─ 3 ─┐

foun - tain with - in, _____ leap -ing

up to give e - ter - nal

life, to give e -

to REFRAIN

ter - nal life. _____

194

God Is So Good

(A Communion Psalm)

Refrain: An African
Christian Melody

Verses: CAREY LANDRY

God is so good; God is so good; God is so good; oh! so good to us! _____

1. Taste, oh taste and see
   The goodness of the Lord;
   With the best of wheat
   He feeds us all.

2. The Lord is our shepherd,
   Nothing shall we want.
   He has prepared
   A banquet for us.

3. The eyes of all look hopefully to You,
   And You give us food in due season:
   Living Bread, the Gift of the earth,
   Fruit of the vine to drink.

4. My soul longs for You, my God,
   As a deer longs for water;
   I will go to the altar of God,
   The God of my gladness and joy.

Copyright © 1982 by NALR. 10802 N. 23rd Ave., Phoenix, Arizona 85029.
All rights reserved.

Hail, Holy Queen

195

TEXT: Salve Regina:
Hermanus Contractus,
late 11th Century.
USE: Feast of our Lady;
Evening Prayer.

LUCIEN DEISS

Hail, Ho-ly Queen, Moth-er of mer-cy,

our __ life, our sweet-ness and our hope.

Hail, __ Ho-ly Queen! Chil-dren of Eve, we

cry to you in our ex-ile. To

you we di-rect our sighs, mourn-ing and

weep-ing in this val-ley of tears.

Copyright © 1982 by Lucien Deiss. Published exclusively by NALR. 10802 N. 23rd
Ave., Phoenix, Arizona 85029. All rights reserved.

You, our Ad-vo-cate, turn to us — your — eyes

full of mer - cy. And af - ter — the ex - ile

of this life, show to us Je - sus, the bless-ed

fruit of your love. O mer - ci - ful Moth - er!

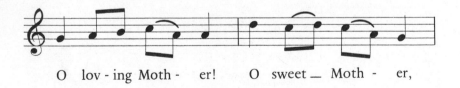

O lov - ing Moth - er! O sweet — Moth - er,

Vir - gin — Ma - ry!

The Hand of the Lord 196

CAREY LANDRY

The hand of the Lord feeds us. He an - swers all our needs.

Last time only - repeat REFRAIN

1. Come, come, come to the table;
   Come, come, eat of the Bread of Life!

2. Come, come, though you have no money;
   Come, come, come without paying;
   Come without cost: eat of the Bread of Life!
   We eat of the Bread of Life!

3. This is the Living Bread;
   This is the Saving Cup;
   One Bread, one Cup for us,
   And we, though many, are one,
   Forever we are one.

4. Listen and come to Him.
   Listen and you shall live.
   This is the Bread of Life
   And they who eat shall live,
   Forever shall they live.

Copyright ©1980 by NALR. 10802 N. 23rd Ave., Phoenix, Arizona 85029.
All rights reserved.

197 He Has Anointed Me

MIKE BALHOFF
GARY DAIGLE
DARRYL DUCOTE

VERSE 1:

1. To bring glad tid - ings to the low - ly, to heal the bro - ken heart,___ He has ___ a - noint - ed me. To pro - claim lib - er - ty to cap - tives, re - lease to pris - on - ers, ___ He has ___ a - noint - ed me.

Copyright © 1981 by Damean Music. Published exclusively by NALR. 10802 N. 23rd Ave., Phoenix, Arizona 85029. All rights reserved.

REFRAIN

The Spir - it __ of God __ is up -
on me, _____ He has __ a
noint - ed me. _____

VERSE 2:

2. To an - nounce a year __ of fa -
- vor, __ to com -fort those _ who mourn, _
He has __ a -
noint - ed me. To
give to them the oil __ of glad - ness, and
share a man - tle of joy,

to REFRAIN

He has_ a - noint - ed me.

255

198 Here I Am, Lord

DAN SCHUTTE, S.J.

VERSES:

1. I, the Lord of sea and sky,

I have heard My peo - ple cry.

All who dwell in dark and sin

My hand will save.

I Who made the stars of night,

I will make their dark - ness bright.

Who will bear My light to them?

Copyright©1981 by Daniel L. Schutte, S.J., and NALR, 10802 N. 23rd Ave., Phoenix, Arizona 85029. All rights reserved.

to REFRAIN

Whom shall I send? _____

REFRAIN

Here I am, Lord. _____ Is it I, Lord? _____ I have heard You call-ing in the night. _____ I will go, Lord, _____ if You lead me. _____ I will hold Your peo-ple in my heart.

2.

I, the Lord of snow and rain,
I have borne My people's pain.
I have wept for love of them.
They turn away.

I will break their hearts of stone,
Give them hearts for love alone.
I will speak My word to them.
Whom shall I send?

3.

I, the Lord of wind and flame,
I will tend the poor and lame,
I will set a feast for them.
My hand will save.

Finest bread I will provide
Till their hearts be satisfied.
I will give My life to them.
Whom shall I send?

199   Holy, Holy, Holy Lord

Suggestion for performance:
The ANTIPHON "Hosanna," measures 1 to 5, may be sung 6 times. The 2nd, 3rd and 5th times, the ANTIPHON is sung *P* as harmonic background for *VERSES 1, 2* and *3* which are sung by a soloist or a group of soloists. They begin on the second beat of measure 2 of the ANTIPHON.

Copyright © 1982 by Lucien Deiss. Published exclusively by NALR. 10802 N. 23rd Ave., Phoenix, Arizona 85029. All rights reserved.

high - est! Lord ____ we give You thanks ____

1. ho - ly ho - ly ____ Lord, ____ God of

2. earth are ___ full ____ of Your glo -

3. He who ___ comes ____ in the name ___

Last time only

and we bless You. Ho -

1. pow'r and might. *(To Verse 2)*

2. - - ry. *(To Antiphon)*

3. of the Lord. ____ *(To Antiphon)*

200   The House Built on the Rock

TEXT: Matthew 7:24-27.
USE: Celebration of the Word;
     Hymn for all times.

♩ = 66

LUCIEN DEISS

ANTIPHON

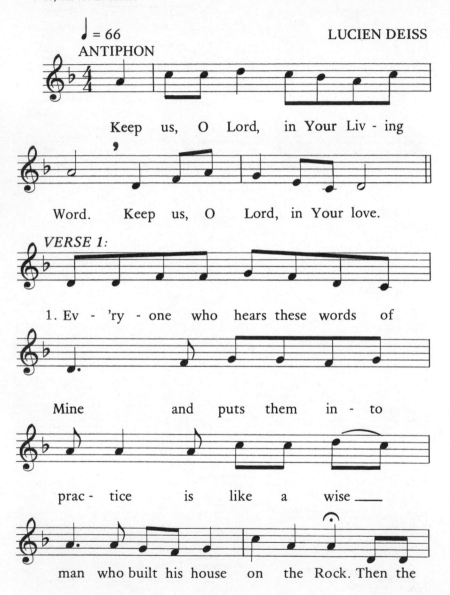

Keep us, O Lord, in Your Liv - ing

Word. Keep us, O Lord, in Your love.

VERSE 1:

1. Ev - 'ry - one who hears these words of

Mine   and puts them in - to

prac - tice is like a wise ____

man who built his house on the Rock. Then the

Copyright © 1982 by Lucien Deiss. Published exclusively by NALR. 10802 N. 23rd
Ave., Phoenix, Arizona 85029. All rights reserved.

rain fell down, tor -rents came rush - ing down, and the

gales blew a - round, un -

leash - ing their might, rag- ing a - gainst __ the

house. But it did not fall, for

(To Antiphon)

it had been __ found - ed on the Rock.

VERSE 2:

2. Ev - 'ry - one who hears these words of

Mine and does not put them in - to

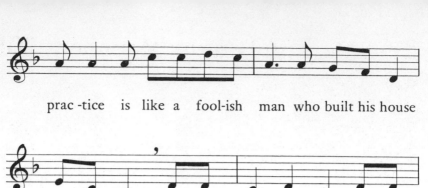

prac-tice is like a fool-ish man who built his house

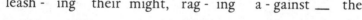

on the sand. Then the rain fell down, tor-rents

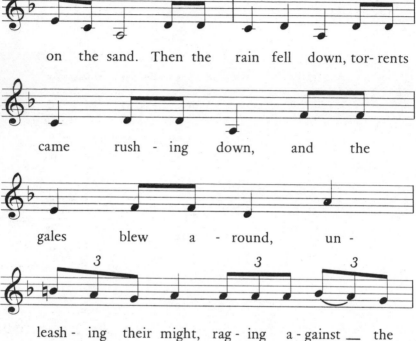

came rush - ing down, and the

gales blew a - round, un -

leash - ing their might, rag - ing a - gainst __ the

house. And it fell with a great crash, for

(To Antiphon)

it had not been found- ed on the Rock.

How Beautiful on the Mountains 201

TEXT: Antiphon: Isaiah 52:7.
Verses: Matthew 4:17; 11:5; 28:18-20.
USE: Ascension; Pentecost; Mission; Vocations.

With Majesty ♩ = 66   LUCIEN DEISS

How beau-ti-ful up-on the moun-tains,—

— the feet of those who

car-ry Good News of sal-va-tion,——

— who pro-claim the reign of God and its peace.

VERSES:

1.   All   the pow'r has been
2.   Bring the joy of sal-
3.   Spread the news that all

Copyright © 1982 by Lucien Deiss. Published exclusively by NALR. 10802 N. 23rd Ave., Phoenix, Arizona 85029. All rights reserved.

giv - en un - to Me in heav -
va - tion to the poor. Re - demp -
cap - tives have been freed. Sing out ___

___ en and on earth. Go pro -
___ tion has been won. Let your
___ with joy - ous songs. In all

claim the Good News, make dis -
hearts o - pen wide, for the
lands where you go, you will

ci - ples ev- 'ry-where. ___
King- dom is at hand. ___ } 1. - 3. And
be My wit -ness-es. ___

I am ev - er with you all the

(To Antiphon)

days, un - til the end of time.

264

Hymn of Initiation

202

Text:
OMER WESTENDORF

Music:
ROBERT E. KREUTZ

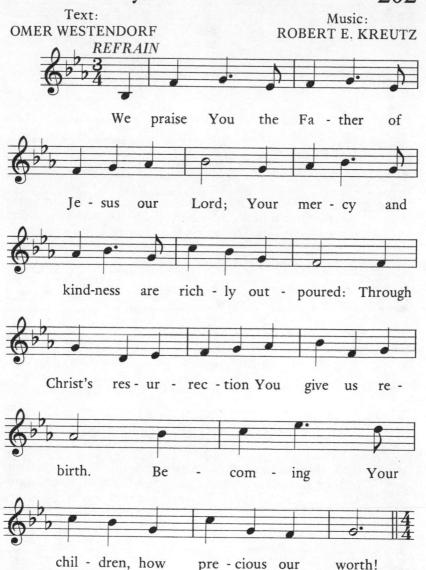

REFRAIN

We praise You the Fa - ther of Je - sus our Lord; Your mer - cy and kind-ness are rich - ly out - poured: Through Christ's res - ur - rec - tion You give us re - birth. Be - com - ing Your chil - dren, how pre - cious our worth!

Copyright ©1982 by NALR. 10802 N. 23rd Ave., Phoenix, Arizona 85029.
All rights reserved.

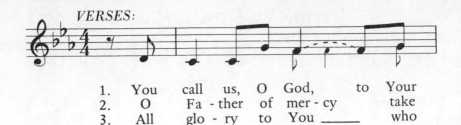

1. You call us, O God, to Your
2. O Fa - ther of mer - cy take
3. All glo - ry to You ____ who

lov-ing em-brace By cleans - ing our souls in the
in - to Your fold, To bless and to pros-per, these
gave us Your son, Through whom our new life and sal -

wa-ters of grace. In faith then we ask You, O
new-ly en - rolled; While we as Your fam-'ly ____
va - tion are won; Who sends us the Spir-it that

Fa - ther a-bove, Pour forth from the foun-tain Your
wel-come them in And wit - ness their heav-en -ward
fills all the earth, And pours out His gifts in our

to REFRAIN

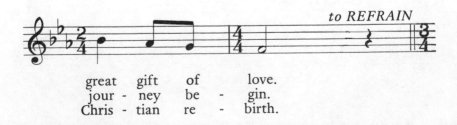

great gift of love.
jour - ney be - gin.
Chris - tian re - birth.

I Am the Resurrection 203

MIKE BALHOFF
DARRYL DUCOTE
GARY DAIGLE

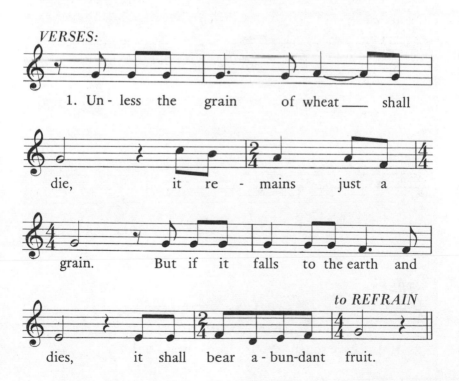

REFRAIN

I am the Re - sur - rec - tion,
I am the Life. Those who be-lieve in Me shall live.

VERSES:

1. Un - less the grain of wheat ___ shall
die, it re - mains just a
grain. But if it falls to the earth and

to REFRAIN

dies, it shall bear a - bun-dant fruit.

Copyright © 1981 by Damean Music. Published exclusively by NALR. 10802 N. 23rd
Ave., Phoenix, Arizona 85029. All rights reserved.

2. If you cling to life you will lose
   All you ever held as dear.
   While if you lose your life for Me,
   You will gain eternal joy.

3. All who wish to serve Me,
   Come and follow after Me.
   And the Father will honor you
   Who serve Me all your lives.

204   I Long for You

MIKE BALHOFF
DARRYL DUCOTE
GARY DAIGLE

I long— for You, O Lord, with all my

First and last time only - repeat REFRAIN.

soul,   I thirst for You.

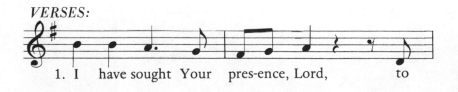

1. I have sought Your pres-ence, Lord, to

Copyright © 1981 by Damean Music. Published exclusively by NALR. 10802 N. 23rd Ave., Phoenix, Arizona 85029. All rights reserved.

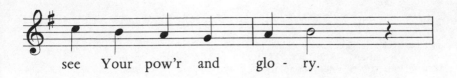

see Your pow'r and glo - ry.

Lord, Your kind - ness is so great;

to REFRAIN

I shall sing Your praise.

2. Thus will I bless You while I live,
And I will call Your name, Lord.
As with the riches of a feast,
My soul is filled by You.

3. Through the night I remember You,
For You have been my Savior.
In the shadow of Your wings
I will shout for joy.

205   I Saw the Living Water

TEXT: Ezekiel 47:12; John 4:23-24;
        Revelation 5:6-12, 7:17; 21:22-23.
USE: Eastertime; Sunday Celebrations;
        Sprinkling of Holy Water.

LUCIEN DEISS

1. I saw the liv-ing wa-ter
2. I saw the Lamb in heav-en,
3. I saw the roy-al Shep-herd
4. I saw the glo-rious tem-ple

flow-ing from the heart of Christ.
wounds a-spar-kle like the stars.
gath-er in-to one His flock,
bright-ened by the ris-en Lord.

Al-le-lu ia, ____ Al-le-lu -
Al-le-lu ia, ____ Al-le-lu -
Al-le-lu ia, ____ Al-le-lu -
Al-le-lu ia, ____ Al-le-lu -

ia!   Those who are
ia!   Those who be -
ia!   Those with His
ia!   A - dore in

Copyright © 1982 by Lucien Deiss. Published exclusively by NALR. 10802 N. 23rd Ave., Phoenix, Arizona 85029. All rights reserved.

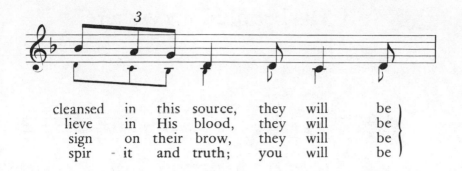

cleansed in this source, they will be
lieve in His blood, they will be
sign on their brow, they will be
spir - it and truth; you will be

1. - 4. saved and sing in joy : Al- le - lu -

ia! Al - le - lu - ia!

Al - le - lu - ia!

Al - le - lu - ia!

Al - le - lu - ia!

206 In His People Everywhere

JOE PINSON

1. We see God in His peo-ple ev-'ry-where; ___ we see God in His peo-ple ev-'ry-where. ___ When His peo - ple ___ love and care, ___ we see God in His peo - ple ev - 'ry - where. ___

2. We hear God in His people everywhere;
We hear God in His people everywhere.
When His music fills the air,
We hear God in His people everywhere.

3. We feel God in His people everywhere;
We feel God in His people everywhere.
When His people give and share,
We feel God in His people everywhere.

Copyright © 1981 by NALR, 10802 N, 23rd Ave., Phoenix, Arizona 85029.
All rights reserved.

In Those Days

207

USE: Eastertime; Sunday Celebrations.

LUCIEN DEISS

Lively ♩ = 132 *(Lower notes - Harmony)*

1. - 5. In those days, the Lord pro-claimed to His dis-ci-ples the Good News of the King-dom.

1. "I
2. "I
3. "I
4. "I
5. "O

am the Way, the Truth, the Life!" *(Jn. 14:6)*
am your peace, I bring you joy!" *(CF Jn 20:20)*
am the bread that comes from heav'n!" *(Jn. 6:51)*
am the life which con - quers death!" *(Jn 11:25)*
come to Me, I give you rest!" *(Mt. 11:28)*

Copyright © 1982 by Lucien Deiss. Published exclusively by NALR. 10802 N. 23rd Ave., Phoenix, Arizona 85029. All rights reserved.

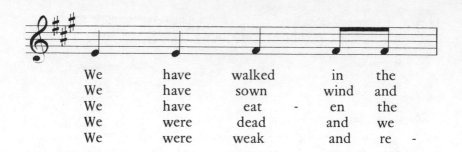

We   have   walked   in   the
We   have   sown   wind   and
We   have   eat - en   the
We   were   dead   and   we
We   were   weak   and   re -

dark - ness and   en - coun - tered lies.
fire   and we   have reaped our wars.
bread   of sad - ness and of sin.
let   the flame of   love die out.
fused   to bat - tle for Your reign.

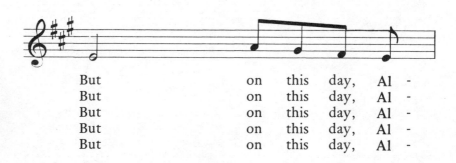

But   on this day, Al -
But   on this day, Al -
But   on this day, Al -
But   on this day, Al -
But   on this day, Al -

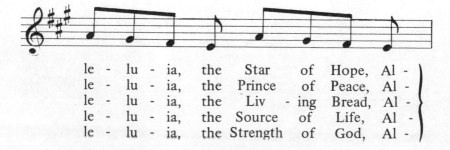

le - lu - ia, the Star   of Hope, Al -
le - lu - ia, the Prince of Peace, Al -
le - lu - ia, the Liv - ing Bread, Al -
le - lu - ia, the Source of Life, Al -
le - lu - ia, the Strength of God, Al -

1.-5. le - lu - ia, is ris - en from the

tomb, is ris- en from the tomb. Al - le - lu - ia, Al -

le - lu-ia, Al - le-lu-ia! Je-sus Christ is Lord! Al -

le - lu - ia, Al - le - lu - ia, Al -

le - lu- ia! Je-sus Christ is Lord! Je-sus Christ is

Lord! Je-sus Christ is Lord!

208 In Your Love Remember Me

THOMAS J. KENDZIA

REFRAIN

In You I hope all the day_ long,___ be -

cause of Your good - ness, O Lord. Re -

mem-ber the love,_ You've shown from of old,_ in Your

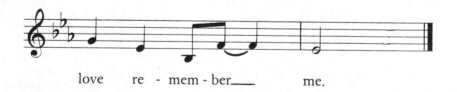

love re - mem - ber___ me.

Copyright © 1980 by NALR. 10802. N. 23rd Ave., Phoenix, Arizona 85029.
All rights reserved.

VERSE 1:

1. Do not let me down, protect me from my foes. Turn to
me for I am weak; my
eyes are always on You.

to REFRAIN

VERSE 2:

2. What joy is life in
You, what peace is life in
You. For You alone give me
joy and peace, You alone are Lord

to REFRAIN

277

209

Jesus Christ Is Lord

(Hymn of the Philippians)

♩ = 66

LUCIEN DEISS

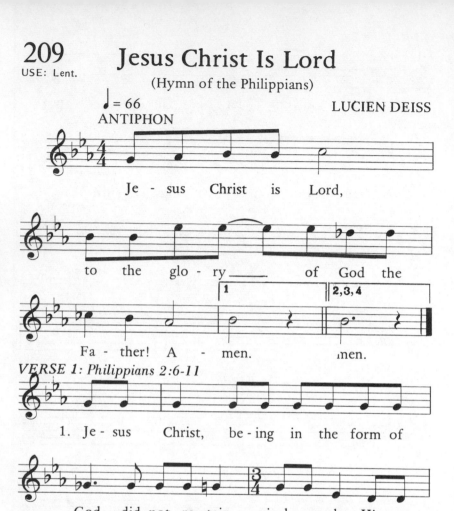

ANTIPHON

Je - sus Christ is Lord,

to the glo - ry ___ of God the

1

2,3,4

Fa - ther! A - men. men.

VERSE 1: Philippians 2:6-11

1. Je - sus Christ, be - ing in the form of

God, did not re - tain jeal - ous - ly His e -

VERSE 2:

qual - i - ty with God. 2. But He emp - tied Him -

self, tak - ing the form of a slave,

Copyright © 1982 by Lucien Deiss. Published exclusively by NALR. 10802 N. 23rd Ave. Phoenix, Arizona 85029. All rights reserved.

(To Antiphon)

be - ing born in hu - man like - ness.

VERSE 3:

3. Be - ing found in hu - man form, ___

He hum-bled Him - self and be-came o -

(To Antiphon)

be - dient to death, e - ven death on the cross.

VERSE 4:

4. There - fore God ex - alt - ed Him, ___

___ and be - stowed on Him the

name a - bove ev - 'ry oth - er

name, so that at Je-sus' name ev - 'ry knee must

bend in the heav-ens and on earth, and un-der the

(To Antiphon)

earth, and ev - 'ry tongue pro - claim:

210 Jesus the Lord

ROC O'CONNOR, S.J.

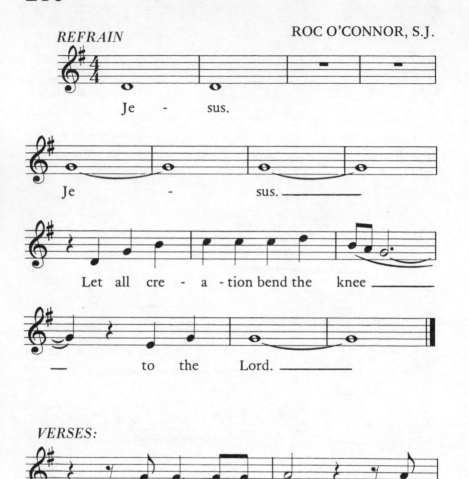

REFRAIN

Je - sus.

Je - sus.

Let all cre - a - tion bend the knee to the Lord.

VERSES:

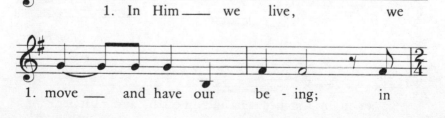

1. In Him we live, we 1. move and have our be - ing; in

Copyright©1981 by Robert F. O'Connor, S.J., and NALR, 10802 N. 23rd Ave., Phoenix, Arizona 85029. All rights reserved.

1. Him — the Christ, — in Him — the

to REFRAIN

1. King! Je - sus, — the Lord. _____

2. Though Son,
   He did not cling to godliness,
   But emptied Himself,
   Became a slave!
   Jesus, the Lord

3. He lived obediently
   His Father's will
   Accepting His death,
   Death on a tree!
   Jesus, the Lord.

211 The Kingdom of God

TEXT: Mark 1:15.
USE: Celebration of the Word of God.

LUCIEN DEISS

♩ = 66

ANTIPHON

The King-dom of God is at hand: Al - le - lu - ia! _____ Re-pent and be - lieve in the Good News of Christ!

VERSES:

1. Your ho - ly Word, O Lord, brings us news of Your joy.__
2. Your ho - ly Word, O Lord, has cre - at - ed the earth.__
3. Your ho - ly Word, O Lord, calls Your chil - dren to life.__
4. Your ho - ly Word, O Lord, shines its light on the world.__
5. Your ho - ly Word, O Lord, feeds the fire of Your love.__
6. Your ho - ly Word, O Lord, from the Vir - gin was born.__

Your Liv - ing Word, O
Your Liv - ing Word, O
Your Liv - ing Word, O
Your Liv - ing Word, O
Your Liv - ing Word, O
Your Liv - ing Word, O

Copyright © 1982 by Lucien Deiss. Published exclusively by NALR, 10802 N. 23rd Ave., Phoenix, Arizona 85029. All rights reserved.

Lord, is the glad-ness of our lives.
Lord, re-cre-ates our hearts a-new.
Lord, plants with-in us seeds of life.
Lord, is the bright-ness in our night.
Lord, is the flam-ing sword of truth.
Lord, is Your ris-en son, our Christ.

Lamb of God 212

TEXT: John 1:29.
USE: Breaking of the Bread.

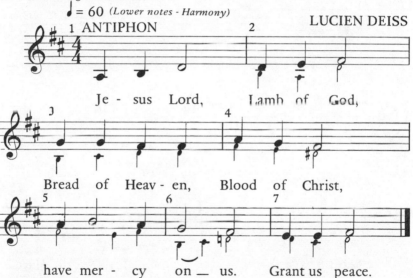

Je-sus Lord, Lamb of God,

Bread of Heav-en, Blood of Christ,

have mer-cy on — us. Grant us peace.

Suggestion for performance:
The ANTIPHON "Lamb of God," measures 1-6, is sung 4 times.
The 2nd, 3rd, and 4th times, measures 1-4 are used as harmonic
background for *VERSES 1, 2* and *3*.

The *VERSES* are sung by a soloist or a group of soloists. They
begin on the 4th beat of measure 1 and end with measure 6.
The song finishes with the conclusion, "Grant us peace" (measure 7).

Copyright © 1982 by Lucien Deiss. Published exclusively by NALR. 10802 N. 23rd
Ave., Phoenix, Arizona 85029. All rights reserved.

Soloist(s)

1. Lamb —— of God, You take a-way the sins of the world. Have mer - cy on us. ——

2. Lamb —— of God, You take a - way the sins of the world. Have mer-cy on us. —— 3. Lamb —— of God, You take a - way the sins of the

284

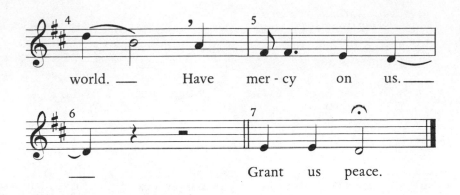

world. — Have mer - cy on us. —

Grant us peace.

Let the Earth Resound 213

TEXT: Psalm 150.

♪ = 184

LUCIEN DEISS

ANTIPHON (Lower notes - Harmony)

Let the earth re - sound with His song!

Let all na - tions praise His love with

danc- ing and sing -ing to Him, our mar-vel-ous Lord!

Copyright © 1982 by Lucien Deiss. Published exclusively by NALR. 10802 N. 23rd Ave., Phoenix, Arizona 85029. All rights reserved.

Suggestion for performance:
The ANTIPHON "Let the earth," is sung 11 times. The 2nd, 4th, 6th, 8th and 10th times, it is sung *P* and used as harmonic background for the *VERSES*.

VERSE 1 begins on measure 6 the first time the ANTIPHON is sung, continues through measures 1 through 7 of the second time and ends on measure 1 of the third time. *VERSE 2* begins on measure 6, and so on.

If the instrumental part is used as *VERSE 6,* the ANTIPHON is sung 13 times with the flute beginning on measure 5 of the 11th time.

VERSES.

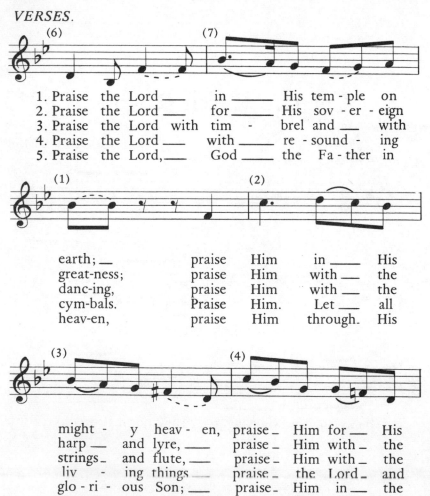

1. Praise the Lord ___ in ____ His tem - ple on
2. Praise the Lord ___ for____ His sov - er - eign
3. Praise the Lord with tim - brel and ___ with
4. Praise the Lord ___ with ____ re - sound - ing
5. Praise the Lord, ___ God ____ the Fa - ther in

earth; __ praise Him in ___ His
great-ness; praise Him with __ the
danc-ing, praise Him with __ the
cym-bals. Praise Him. Let __ all
heav-en, praise Him through. His

might - y heav - en, praise_ Him for __ His
harp __ and lyre, ____ praise_ Him with _ the
strings_ and flute, ___ praise _ Him with _ the
liv - ing things ___ praise_ the Lord_ and
glo - ri - ous Son; ___ praise_ Him in __ the

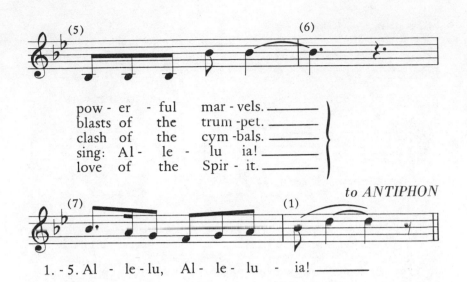

pow - er - ful mar - vels. _____
blasts of the trum - pet. _____
clash of the cym - bals. _____
sing: Al - le - lu - ia! _____
love of the Spir - it. _____

to ANTIPHON

1. - 5. Al - le - lu, Al - le - lu - ia! _____

Lift Up Your Hearts 214

ROC O'CONNOR, S.J.

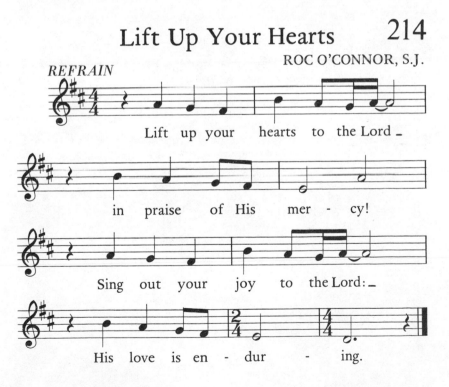

REFRAIN

Lift up your hearts to the Lord _

in praise of His mer - cy!

Sing out your joy to the Lord: _

His love is en - dur - ing.

Copyright©1981 by Robert F. O'Connor, S.J., and NALR, 10802 N. 23rd Ave.,
Phoenix, Arizona 85029. All rights reserved.

VERSES:

1. Shout with joy __ to the Lord, all the earth!

Praise the glo - ry of His name! Say to God, "How

to REFRAIN

won -drous Your works, how glo-rious Your name!"

2. Let the earth worship, singing Your praise.
   Praise the glory of Your name!
   Come and see the deeds of the Lord!
   Come, worship His name!

3. At His touch the dry land did appear;
   Paths were opened in the sea,
   Let the earth rejoice in His might,
   The might of His love.

4. Listen now all you servants of God,
   As I tell of His great works.
   Blessed be the Lord of my life!
   His love shall endure!

Light of the World 215

THOMAS J. KENDZIA

VERSES 1 & 2:

1. Mak - ing your way ___
2. Now is the time ___

to plac - es un - known, ___
to make up your mind, ___

is so much hard -
to fol - low the light ___

- er ___ when you're all a - lone, ___
___ that ___ bright - ens up your day, ___

on your own. ___
ev - 'ry way. ___

And when it seems ___
Just lis - ten to Him, ___

Copyright ©1980 by NALR. 10802 N. 23rd Ave., Phoenix, Arizona 85029.
All rights reserved.

like there's no one
He'll nev - er_____ steer you

there, you just o - pen your eyes ___
wrong, so get up and

to REFRAIN

___ and you will see._____
fol - low a - long._____

REFRAIN

You _____ are the Light ___ of the world, ___

___ shine Your Light _____ on

me._____ O, _____ love as ___

bright as the sun_____ shin - ing down ___

___ on ev - 'ry-one._____

3. What do we need ____
to make us be - lieve? ____
Who else could do ____ what He does? _
____
Who else could love ____
the way He loves, ____
dark - ness no more ____ in His
Light ____ let _ us sing. _

to REFRAIN

216 Lord, Send Out Your Spirit

MIKE BALHOFF
GARY DAIGLE
DARRYL DUCOTE

REFRAIN

Lord, send out Your Spir-it, and re-new the face of the earth. ____

VERSES:

1. Bless the Lord, my soul, You are great in-deed. __ You are clothed with ma-jes-ty and light.

to REFRAIN

You are clothed with ma-jes-ty and light.

Copyright © 1981 by Damean Music. Published exclusively by NALR. 10802 N. 23rd Ave., Phoenix, Arizona 85029. All rights reserved.

2. Wonderful Your works, You have made them all.
   In Your wisdom You have fashioned all.
   In Your wisdom You have fashioned all.

3. You have set the springs to wash the land,
   You have made the earth full of life.
   You have made the earth full of life.

4. Send Your Spirit, Lord and make us new.
   Recreate the face of the earth.
   Recreate the face of the earth.

5. May Your glory last till the end of time.
   I will sing Your praise while I live.
   I will sing Your praise while I live.

Lord, to Whom Shall We Go? 217

TOM CONRY

REFRAIN

Lord, to whom shall we go? You a-
lone have a word that may live be-yond our grave.

VERSES 1, 2 and 3:

1. More than peo-ple can say, You are our
2. As long as peo-ple shall live, You are our
3. Wher-ev-er peo-ple are fed, You are our

Copyright © 1980 by NALR. 10802 N. 23rd Ave., Phoenix, Arizona 85029.
All rights reserved.

way, ____ and our walk - ing. ____ Your Word is
gift, ____ and our giv - ing. ____ Your Word is
breath, ____ and our breath - ing. ____ Your Word is

al-ways be - fore me, as fire in the sky
al-ways with- in me, as wa - ter in the earth
al-ways a -round me, just as air sur-rounds us all

to REFRAIN

Be - yond the day I die.
Since be - fore my birth.
We may hear Your call.

VERSE 4:

4. When- ev - er peo-ple ask why, You are our

cry, ____ and our call - ing. ____ Your Word will

al-ways en - fold me, and hold me close to You.

Here in the world, now while I live, You are my

294

Here in the world, now

God. _____

while I live, You are my

God. _____ *to REFRAIN*

Here in the world, now while I live.

The Love of God 218

TEXT: Antiphon: Romans 5:5.
Verses; 1 Corinthians 13·47.
USE: Holy Spirit themes; 3rd Sunday of Lent, A;
4th Sunday, Ordinary Time, C.

LUCIEN DEISS

ANTIPHON ♩ = 72 *(Lower notes - Harmony)*

The love of God is poured

forth in -to our hearts through the Ho - ly Spir - it,

Whom He gave to us to be the song of our lives.

Copyright © 1982 by Lucien Deiss. Published exclusively by NALR. 10802 N. 23rd
Ave., Phoenix, Arizona 85029. All rights reserved.

1. Love   is ____   pa - tient,
2. Love   is   not   proud, ____
3. Love   is   not   spite - ful,
4. Love   bears ____   all ____   things,

love ____   is   kind. ____
is ____   not   rude. ____
al -   ways   par - dons,
al -   ways   trusts. ____

Love   is   not   jeal - ous,
Love   is   not   self - ish,
does   not   de - light - in   wrong,
Love   hopes ____   ev - 'ry   thing,

nor   is   it   boast - ful.
nor   eas - 'ly   an - gered.
re - joic - es   in   the   truth.
and   it   en - dures ____   all.

(To Antiphon)

1. - 4. Love   will nev- er pass   a - way.

May the Lord Bless You 219

CHERYL ANN FURTAK, C.S.F.N.

REFRAIN

May the Lord bless you; — may the Lord keep you. — May the Lord's face shine up-on you; — may the Lord look kind-ly, — may He look gra-cious-ly; may the Lord give you — His peace. —

VERSES:

1. May the Lord — al-ways greet you at morn-ing. — May He rest in your soul at night. —

Copyright ©1981 by NALR. 10802 N. 23rd Ave., Phoenix, Arizona 85029.
All rights reserved.

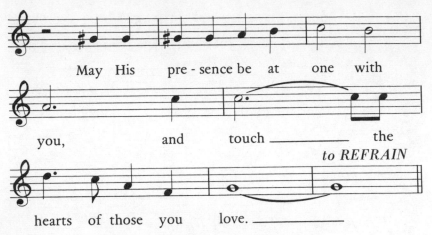

May His pre - sence be at one with you, and touch _____ the

to REFRAIN

hearts of those you love. _____

2. May His love fill you with graces.
   May His Spirit set you free.
   May His tenderness teach you,
   Gently, to walk as a child of light.

3. Though You go now,
   Your Spirit remains with me.
   You have found a place in my soul.
   Now I thank You for all that's been,
   And for all to come, I say "Yes."

220   May We Praise You

JOHN FOLEY, S.J.

1. May we praise You, O Lord, with
(2. May our) liv - ing be true. May
(3. Let Your) step guide our path. Let
(4. To the) Fa - ther be praise; to

heart and hand and voice. And since
all re - turn to You. And when
shades of dark not last. May the
Son and Spir - it, praise. Un - to

Copyright©1981 by John B. Foley, S.J., and NALR, 10802 N. 23rd Ave.,
Phoenix, Arizona 85029. All rights reserved.

life it-self is Your gift to us, ___ then may
life is done let our pass - ing be ___ like a
sun of jus - tice re - turn on high, ___ and Your
God the one let all praise be done, ___ till the

1, 2, 3

all that we are be 1. Yours.
birth in - to light of 2. day.
love be our road and 3. guide.
dawn of the last - ing

4

2. May our 4. day, _____ may we
3. Let Your
4. To the

praise. ___

My People 221

In a chant style (Allegro)

Sr. CATHERINE MILLER
arr. by Tutti Camarata

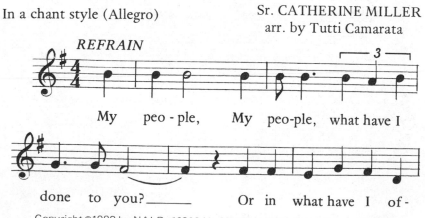

REFRAIN

3

My peo - ple, My peo - ple, what have I

done to you? ___ Or in what have I of -

Copyright ©1982 by NALR. 10802 N. 23rd Ave., Phoenix, Arizona 85029.
All rights reserved.

fend - ed you?＿＿＿ An - swer Me.

1. I led you to the heart of God,
   But you led Me to Pilate's court.

2. I healed your wounds with tenderness,
   But you strike Me and scourge Me.

3. I led you to the way of freedom,
   But you led Me to the cross.

4. I opened the Truth before you,
   But you open My side with a lance.

222 O, That I Had a Thousand Voices

Composite JOHANN MENTZER   THOMAS F. SAVOY

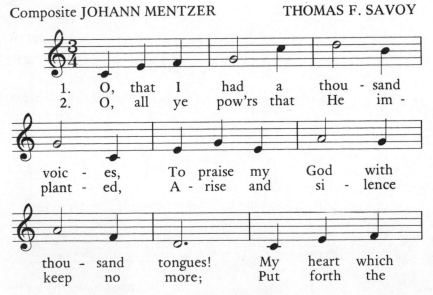

1. O, that I had a thou - sand voic - es, To praise my God with thou - sand tongues! My heart which
2. O, all ye pow'rs that He im - plant - ed, A - rise and si - lence keep no more; Put forth the

Copyright©1982 by NALR, 10802 N. 23rd Ave., Phoenix, Arizona 85029.
All rights reserved.

in   the   Lord   re - joic - es
grace   that   He   hath   grant - ed;

Would then pro - claim in   grate - ful
Your no - blest work   is   to ___   a -

songs.   To   all,   wher - ev - er
dore.   O   soul   and   bod - y

I ___ might be,   What great things
be ___ ye   meet   With heart - felt

God   hath done   for   me.
praise your Lord   to   greet!

223 The Ones I Love

CAREY LANDRY

VERSES 1, 2, 4 and 6:

1. The ones I love are man-y col-ored. The ones I love are flow-ers bright. The ones I love are gifts e-ter-nal. The ones I love have shared their light.

2. The ones I love are part of me.
The ones I love have shared my heart.
The ones I love have heard my story.
The ones I love have felt my pain.

Copyright © 1980 by NALR. 10802 N. 23rd ave., Phoenix, Arizona 85029.
All rights reserved.

4. The ones I love have shared their sorrows.
The ones I love have told their fears.
The ones I love have held me closely.
The ones I love have dried my tears.

6. The ones I love have brought me courage.
The ones I love have brought me peace.
The ones I love have been my freedom.
The ones I love brought me new birth.

VERSES 3, 5 and 7:

3. Oh I can't get us all in-to a sen-tence, and I can't neat-ly pack-age all they mean; for

Last time to Coda

lines of words would ne-ver catch com-plete-ly— all that they mean——— to

(D.C.) *Coda*

me. 4. The ones I

7. Thank you for the gifts of the ones I love.

Thank you for the gifts of the ones I love.

5. I believe there'll be no goodbyes in heaven,
   I believe there will only be hellos.
   For all the hours we've spent here together
   Are only the beginning of our joy.

7. And though I can't get us all into a sentence,
   Though I can't neatly package all they mean;
   I stand before you, Lord, I say thank you,
   Thank you for the gifts of the ones I love.
   Thank you for the gifts of the ones I love.

224   Only This I Want

DAN SCHUTTE, S.J.

REFRAIN

On - ly this I want:

but to know the Lord,

and to bear His cross, so to

wear the crown He wore.

Cpoyright ©1981 by Daniel L. Schutte, S.J., and NALR, 10802 N. 23rd Ave.,
Phoenix, Arizona 85029. All rights reserved.

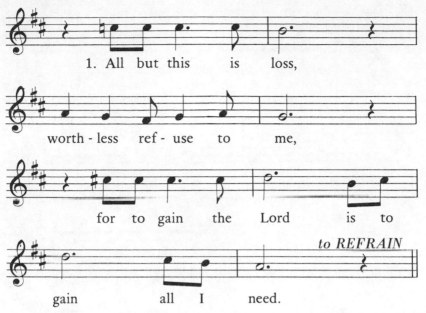

1. All but this is loss,
worth-less ref-use to me,
for to gain the Lord is to
gain all I need.

to REFRAIN

2. I will run the race;
   I will fight the good fight,
   So to win the prize of the Kingdom of my Lord.

3. Let your hearts be glad,
   Always glad in the Lord,
   So to shine like stars in the darkness of the night.

225 Our Life and Our Song

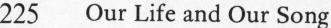

TOM CONRY

VERSES:

1. Je - sus, Son of Mar - y was a car - pen - ter's child, and He knew what it was to be lost and for - got - ten, like the tin - y seed — be -fore it grows and chang - es, strong as the wind and near as our dream - ing.

to REFRAIN

He is our life and our song.

Copyright ©1980 by NALR. 10802 N. 23rd Ave., Phoenix, Arizona 85029.
All rights reserved.

REFRAIN

And like the wind gone a - way,

Last time to ⊕

word and si - lence, He is our life and our song.

⊕ *Coda*

He is our life and our song.

Word and si - lence, He is our life and our song.

2. Jesus healed the sick and gave sight to the blind,
   And He knew what it was to live a life for others,
   Entrusting Himself to that awful silence,
   Desperately small, but large as our dreaming.
   He is our life and our song.

3. Jesus was a man that the wind and sea obeyed,
   And He knew what it was to live in the open,
   No home or bed to lay his head down,
   Orphaned by the past and up against tomorrow.
   He is our life and our song.

4. Jesus was a man who stood by His friends,
   But He knew what it was to have the crowd save another,
   And stand alone in a crowded courtroom,
   Cross and grave open before Him.
   He is our life and our song.

5. Jesus was a man that even death couldn't hold,
   So He lives on and on when we sing the story
   Of a stone rolled back and a tomb laid empty,
   He lives on now and forever, for
   He is our life and our song.

307

226 Path of Life

MIKE BALHOFF
GARY DAIGLE
DARRYL DUCOTE

REFRAIN

You will show me the path of life,___

___ and guide me to

joy for - ev - er.

VERSES:

1. Keep me safe, O God,

You are my hope.

You a - lone will be my

to REFRAIN

sav - ing God.

2. You have taught me love, You who fashioned all.
   Wonderful indeed are Your holy ones.

3. I will bless You, Lord, You who counsel me.
   Even in the night I rejoice in You.

4. Now my heart is glad, my soul is filled with joy.
   Never will my Lord abandon me.

Copyright © 1981 by Damean Music. Published exclusively by NALR. 10802 N. 23rd Ave., Phoenix, Arizona 85029. All rights reserved.

Peace I Leave - Lamb of God Medley

227

CAREY LANDRY

Peace I Leave:

Peace I leave,
My peace I give;
Peace for you,
Peace for all.

(Repeat)

Lamb of God:

Lamb of God, You take a - way the sins of the world; have mer - cy on us.

Lamb of God, You take a - way the sins of the world; grant us peace.

Copyright ©1982 by NALR. 10802 N. 23rd Ave., Phoenix, Arizona 85029.
All rights reserved.

228   Praise His Name

THOMAS J. KENDZIA

REFRAIN

Praise the name of the Lord._____

He, a - lone, is our God._____

Mak - er of earth, and heav - en a - bove;__

_____ praise His name._____

VERSES 1 and 2:

1. Come, let us sing to His
2. All the earth re - joice in its

name._____ Sing praise to His
God._____ Let hills bow down __

Copyright ©1980 by NALR. 10802 N. 23rd Ave., Phoenix, Arizona 85029.
All rights reserved.

glo - ri - ous   name. _____
___   to His   name. _____   The

Give   to the   Lord   our   love   and our
val - leys and   seas   rise   up ___   in

lives,   let   us   praise
joy ___   to   praise

to REFRAIN

His   name. _____
His   name. _____

VERSE 3:

3. Come, let   us   o -   pen   our

hearts, _____   to the   Lord ___

___   Who gave us   life. _____

311

Hearts and hands raised high to the

to REFRAIN

Lord let us praise His name. ___

229   Praised Be the Father

MIKE BALHOFF
DARRYL DUCOTE
GARY DAIGLE

REFRAIN

Praised be the Fa - ther of our ___

Lord, Je - sus Christ, Who gave us new

birth, a new hope, ___ by

rais - ing His Son from death. ___

Copyright © 1981 by Damean Music. Published exclusively by NALR. 10802 N. 23rd Ave., Phoenix, Arizona 85029. All rights reserved.

VERSE 1:

1. A birth un - to hope which draws — its life ——— from the res - ur - rec - tion — of Christ from — the dead, ———

to REFRAIN

VERSES 2 and 3:

2. A birth to an — in - her - i -tance, one which will nev - er fade, ———

3. Al - though we've nev - er seen — Him, with-out see - ing we — be - lieve! ———

313

for _____ it is kept in
With _____ great ____ joy, we

heav - en __ for you __ who are
cel - e - brate __ His love __ and __

guard - ed by __ God's pow'r __
sing the Fa - ther's praise __

to REFRAIN

__ through faith.
__ through Christ.

Praised Be the Flower 230

TEXT: Luke 1:42.
USE: Celebration of Our Lady.

LUCIEN DEISS

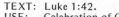

♩ = 63
VERSES:

1.	Praised	be	the	flow'r	which	has
2.	Praised	be	the	dawn	which	has
3.	Praised	be	the	maid	full	of
4.	Praised	be	the	moth -	er	in
5.	Praised	be	the	wom -	an	in
6.	Praised	be	the	Queen	who	as -

bloomed	in	the	gar - den	of	the
come	in	the	ver - y	heart	of
grace,	a -	mong wom -	en	tru -	ly
whom	dwells	the	Spir - it	of	the
tears	who	stood	near the	cross	of
cends,	robed	in	glo - ry	shin - ing	

Lord.	Praised	be	the
night.	Praised	be	the
blest.	Praised	be	the
Lord.	Praised	be	the
Christ.	Praised	be	the
bright.	Praised	be	the

Copyright ©1982 by Lucien Deiss. Published exclusively by NALR.
10802 N. 23rd Ave., Phoenix, Arizona 85029. All rights reserved.

flow'r   which   has   bloomed.
dawn   which   has   come.
maid   full   of   grace.
moth - er   of   Christ.
wom - an   in   tears.
Queen   who   as - cends.

Blessed   be   the   bud   which   has
Blessed   be   the   sun   which   has
Blessed   be   the   girl   loved   by
Blessed   be   the   child   born   from
Blessed   be   the   Moth - er   who
Blessed   be   the   Moth - er   a -

sprung   from   the   root   of   Jes - se's
shone   in   the   midst   of   all   our
God.   With   His   beau - ty   she   is
her.   He   is   hope   for   all   the
wept,   for   her   love   was   cru - ci -
dorned   with   the   stars   and   with   the

(To Antiphon)

vine,   and this bud   is   Je-sus   Christ.
tears,   and this sun   is   Je-sus   Christ.
crowned,   and her crown   is   Je-sus   Christ.
world,   and this child   is   Je-sus   Christ.
fied,   and her love   is   Je-sus   Christ.
sun,   and her splen-dor: Je-sus   Christ.

Mar - y, the Moth - er of Je - sus and ser - vant of the Lord, praise to you! Queen of the earth and of heav - en, we bless your ho-ly Child, Je-sus Christ.

231 Psalm of the Good Shepherd

(Psalm 23)

CAREY LANDRY

REFRAIN

The Lord is my shep - herd: there is noth - ing I shall want.____

VERSES:

1. The Lord ____ is my Shep - herd, I lack for noth -ing at all. ____

____ He leads me to the wa - ters of *to REFRAIN* life; there He re - fresh - es my soul. ____

Copyright ©1982 by NALR. 10802 N. 23rd Ave., Phoenix, Arizona 85029.
All rights reserved.

2. He guides me along the paths that are right,
I fear no evil at all;
For You, O Lord are at my side,
You give me the courage I need.

3. You spread Your table before me
In the sight of my foes;
You anoint my head with oil,
My cup overflows.

4. Only goodness and kindness
Shall follow me all the days of my life.
And I shall live in the house of the Lord
For years upon years to come.

Rainbow

232

DARRYL DUCOTE

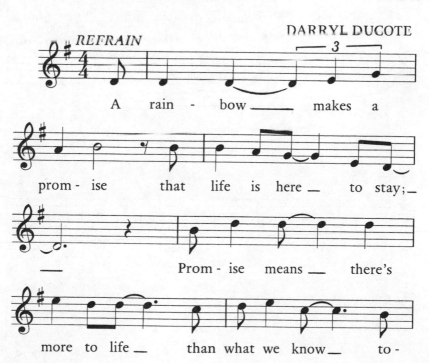

REFRAIN

A rain - bow ___ makes a
prom - ise that life is here ___ to stay; ___
___ Prom - ise means ___ there's
more to life ___ than what we know ___ to -

Copyright © 1973 by Damean Music. Published exclusively by NALR. 10802 N. 23rd Ave., Phoenix, Arizona 85029. All rights reserved.

day._____ I can share _ to-

mor-row, _ if there's one to pledge it to. _

Last time to Coda ⊕

_ I'd like to be _ a

rain-bow _ and prom-ise life _ to you. _

VERSES:

(♭)
1. All the joy_____ we know__
2. There's much that we'll____ dis-cov-

__ now _ has come be-cause we share ;_
- er____ on roads where love will lead;_

di - vid - ing up ___ the sor -
we'll come to know ___ our own ___

- row   makes   it
heart   as   we

eas - i - er ___ to bear. ___
an - swer each ___ one's need. ___

So with our hearts ___ to-geth-
For in the life ___ we prom-

- er ___ life is bound ___ to grow. ___
- ise ___ there's more ___ to what we share; ___

I prom-ise you ___ to - mor -
To lose our-selves ___ in

to REFRAIN

- row _____ from
giv - ing is to

all the love _____ I know. _____
find God hid - den there. _____

Coda

like to be _ a rain - bow _____ and

prom - ise life to

you. _____

Redeemer Lord

233

JOHN FOLEY, S.J.

VERSES:

1. You are our Fa - ther; _____ re - deem - er Lord _____ are You. Why must we wan-der _____ so far a- way _____ from Your truth? O - pen the heav - ens, _____ re - turn to our

Copyright©1981 by John B. Foley, S.J. and NALR, 10802 N. 23rd Ave.,
Phoenix, Arizona 85029. All rights reserved.

side. You are our Fa - ther, Lord, our guide.

2. Come back to Your servants now;
   Give back, O Lord, Your light.
   The pathways are parting now we choose,
   Yet You hide from our sight;
   Rupture the heavens, come back to our lives:
   Come down to Your people, Lord of life. *(Refrain)*

REFRAIN

My shep - herd is the Lord,___ there is
noth - ing I shall need. Fresh and
green __ are the pas-tures where He'll lead. __

3. Your world doesn't know You now;
   They close their eyes to You.
   O where are the wondrous deeds You'd do,
   All for those who were true?
   Sunder the heavens, and come to our aid.
   Lord, look how Your people stand afraid. *(Refrain)*

4. Where is Your answer?
   I cry my days to You.
   A worm and no man am I,
   Despised by all in my gloom.
   Lord, will You hear me, take heed of my heart?
   O why must You let Your love depart? *(Refrain)*

Save Us, O Lord 234

BOB DUFFORD, S.J.

REFRAIN

Save us, O Lord; car - ry us back.

Rouse Your pow-er and come. — Res-cue Your peo-ple;

Show us Your face. Bring us back. __

VERSE 1:

1. O Shep - herd of Is - ra - el,

hear us. ___ Re - turn and we shall be

saved. __ A - rise, O Lord; hear our

to REFRAIN

cries, O Lord: Bring us back!

Copyright©1981 by Robert J. Dufford, S.J., and NALR, 10802 N. 23rd Ave.,
Phoenix, Arizona 85029. All rights reserved.

VERSE 2:

2. How long will You hide from Your peo - ple? ____ We long to see Your face. ____ Give ear to us. Draw near to us, Lord God of hosts!

to REFRAIN

VERSE 3:

3. Turn ____ a - gain; care for Your vine; pro - tect what Your right hand has plant - ed. ____ Your vine -yards are tram- pled, up - root - ed, and burned.

to REFRAIN

Come to us Fa - ther of might! ____

Send Us Your Spirit 235

THOMAS J. KENDZIA

VERSES:

1. We are one in the Spir - it. ____ One in the Lord. ____ Our hearts are filled with You, our lives are one in You. ____

2. There is one bod - y. ____ There is one Spir - it. ____ One Lord, ____ one faith, one God of all. ____

Copyright ©1980 by NALR. 10802 N. 23rd Ave., Phoenix, Arizona 85029.
All rights reserved.

Lord, send us Your Spir - it___ Let us be one___ in You. Keep us in peace___ and fill us with love.___ Lord, send us Your Spir - it.___ Let us re - joice ___ in You. O Lord, how good is Your Spir - it in us, Al - le - lu - ia.___

(D.C.)

Sing Alleluia, Sing 236

GARY AULT

REFRAIN

Sing al - le - lu - ia, sing __

__ al - le - lu - ia, sing al - le - lu- ia to the Lord.__

__ Sing al - le - lu - ia, sing __

__ al - le - lu - ia, sing al -

- le - lu - ia, to the Lord. __

Sing His __ praise, __

Copyright © 1973 by Damean Music. Published exclusively by NALR. 10802 N. 23rd Ave., Phoenix, Arizona 85029. All rights reserved.

sing His — praise! — Sing al -

- le - lu - ia to the Lord. —

VERSES:

1. Let my soul re - joice in the King —
2. When His chil - dren lived in fear, —

as to Him our prais - es we bring, —
God as - sured them He was near, —

sing - ing of His
lead - ing them — in

migh - ty deeds — a - mong all. —
to the prom - ised land. —

1., 2. He is — Lord, He is Lord —

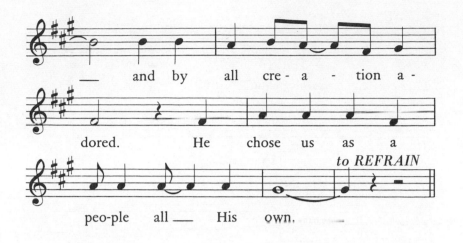

and by all cre-a-tion a-dored. He chose us as a peo-ple all His own.

to REFRAIN

Sing Out in Thanksgiving 237

Text:
WILLARD F. JABUSCH

Music:
ROBERT E. KREUTZ

REFRAIN

Sing out, sing out in thanks-giv-ing. O sing out, sing out in thanks-giv-ing. Sing out, sing out in thanks-giv-ing, For all he's done for us. us, For all he's done for us, For all he's done for us.

Copyright©1981 by NALR, 10802 N. 23rd Ave., Phoenix, Arizona 85029.
Words Copyright 1980 by Fr. Willard F. Jabusch.
All rights reserved.

1. There is one bod - y, one
Spir - it, too, _____ One
Lord, one faith and one
wash- ing; _____ There is one hope that can
strength- en us; _____ One

to REFRAIN

Fa - ther of ___ us all.

2. Now each of us is a sinner here,
    But each is offered forgiveness;
    We have a Savior Who died for us;
    A gift of perfect love.

3. Each man and woman is called by name,
    Is called to be His disciple,
    Is called to come to the supper room;
    To eat the bread of life.

4. Now, some are called to the preaching task,
    And some are called to be shepherds,
    But all are called to the noble work
    Of building up the church.

Song of Abandonment 238

CAREY LANDRY

REFRAIN

Fa-ther, in-to Your hands I com-mend my life.

1. I abandon myself to You;
   Do with me whatever You may will.

2. Whatever You may choose I thank You;
   I am ready for all, I accept all,
   Let only Your will be done in me.

3. I offer it to You with all the love of my heart,
   For I love You, Lord.
   I surrender myself into Your hands,
   Without reserve, with boundless confidence,
   For You are my God.

Copyright ©1980 by NALR. 10802 N. 23rd Ave., Phoenix, Arizona 85029.
All rights reserved.

239 Song of Thanksgiving

(A Eucharistic Prayer)

DARRYL DUCOTE

REFRAIN

Love that's free-ly giv-en wants to free-ly be re-ceived. All the love You've poured on us can hard-ly be be-lieved. And all that we can of-fer You is thanks,

Copyright ©1973 by Damean Music. Published exclusively by NALR.
10802 N. 23rd Ave., Phoenix, Arizona 85029. All rights reserved.

all that we can of-

-fer You ___ is thanks. ___

VERSES:

1. Cre - a - tion tells a sto-

-ry ___ that be - gan so long a - go, ___

of love that longed ___ to

share its life in hope that love would grow. ___

The sun re - peats ___ each morn-

-ing, ___ the sto - ry is ___ re - told, ___

and just in love's __ re - tell -

to REFRAIN

- ing __ new chap-ters yet un - fold. __

2. Your care called out a people
   Your love made them Your own.
   You freed their hearts and calmed their fears
   And finally brought them home.

   It's when our trials are ended
   We most easily forget,
   But Your friendship never ceases
   Your love shows no regret.

3. Our hearts forgot Your story
   So Your Son became its word;
   And gave a sign in bread and wine
   To be sure that we had heard.

   We tried to kill His mem'ry
   But Your love refused to die,
   Now everytime we break this bread
   Love's meaning comes alive.

4. So now we stand in wonder
   Of all Your love has done,
   To hear Your tale and offer thanks
   That we are not alone.

   Just fill us with Your Spirit
   To make Your people one,
   So we can join our story
   To the one told through Your Son.

The Song of the Beatitudes 240

TEXT: Antiphon: Revelation 19:9.
Verses: Matthew 5:3-12.
USE: All Saints.

LUCIEN DEISS

ANTIPHON (Lower notes - Harmony)

How   blest   are   those

who   are   in - vit - ed

to   the   ban - quet   of   the

King - dom!

Copyright © 1982 by Lucien Deiss. Published exclusively by NALR. 10802 N. 23rd Ave., Phoenix, Arizona 85029. All rights reserved.

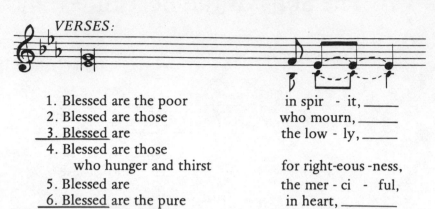

1. Blessed are the poor	in spir - it, _____
2. Blessed are those	who mourn, _____
3. Blessed are	the low - ly, _____
4. Blessed are those	
who hunger and thirst	for right-eous -ness,
5. Blessed are	the mer - ci - ful,
6. Blessed are the pure	in heart, _____
7. Blessed are	the peace -mak -ers,
8. Blessed are those persecuted	for right - eous-ness,
9. Blessed are you	
when you are insulted and per - se -cut - ed, _____	
10. Rejoice and	be glad, _____

for theirs is the	King-dom of heav-en.
for they will	be___ con -soled.__
for they will in -	her - it the land.__
for they will be	sat - is - fied.__
for they	will be shown mer-cy.
for _____	they will see God.__
for they will be called	sons___ of God.__
	(chil-dren)
for theirs is the	King-dom of heav-en.
and when you are	
slandered be -	cause ___ of Me.__
for your reward will be	great ___ in heav-en.

Song of Wonder

Text:
WILLARD F. JABUSCH

Music:
ROBERT E. KREUTZ

1. Lord, ev - 'ry grain of sand,
2. O - ceans that nev - er end,
3. Chil - dren so quick to laugh,
4. Peo - ple with kind - ly hearts,
5. We closed our eyes too long,
6. Lord, we stand full of awe;

ev - 'ry drop of wa - ter,
high - est Him - a - lay - as,
old folks full of wis - dom,
reach - ing out to com - fort,
this we're now re - pent - ing;
see, our hearts are burn - ing!

flow - ers in sum - mer - time,
flights to a dis - tant moon,
all those who dare to love,
tak - ing the time to care,
Light comes through scat - tered clouds,
Teach - er of all that's good

Copyright©1981 by NALR, 10802 N. 23rd Ave., Phoenix, Arizona 85029.
Words Copyright 1980 by Fr. Willard F. Jabusch.
All rights reserved.

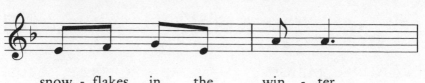

snow - flakes   in   the   win - ter,
pow - er   in   an   a - tom,
mak - ing   brave   de - ci - sions,
mak - ing   oth - ers   hap - py,
now   the   storm's   re - lent - ing,
words   of   praise   we're   learn - ing,

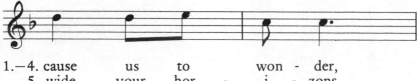

1.—4. cause   us   to   won - der,
5. wide   your   hor - i - zons,
6. lit - tle   by   lit - tle,

1.- 4. cause us now to praise you.

1. God of the
2. God of the
3. God of the
4. God of the

5. splen -did are your se - crets;   won -d'rous are
6. o - pen us to glo - ry   great - ness in

lit - tle things,
might - y things,
hu - man soul,
no - ble deeds,
all your works,
hum - ble clay,

Hal - le - lu - ia.

340

There Is One Lord 242

MIKE BALHOFF
GARY DAIGLE
DARRYL DUCOTE

REFRAIN

There is one Lord, one
faith, one bap - ti - sm, one

*Last time -
repeat REFRAIN*

God and Fa - ther of all.

VERSES:

1. Live a life wor - thy of your

call - ing, in hu - mil - i - ty, meek - ness and

Copyright © 1981 by Damean Music. Published exclusively by NALR. 10802 N. 23rd Ave., Phoenix, Arizona 85029. All rights reserved.

pa - tience,   bear - ing   with one an -

to REFRAIN

oth - er   lov-ing- ly.

2. Make ev'ry effort to preserve
   The unity that comes from the Spirit,
   Joined as one people by your peacefulness.

3. Let us profess the truth in love
   And grow to the fullness of Christ.
   Through Him the whole body is joined as one.

243   This Alone

TIM MANION

REFRAIN

One thing I ask, this a - lone I

seek, _____ to dwell in the house of the

Lord all my days. _____ For one

Copyright©1981 by Timothy J. Manion and NALR, 10802 N. 23rd Ave.,
Phoenix, Arizona 85029. All rights reserved.

day with-in Your tem-ple heals ev-'ry day a-lone. O Lord, bring me to Your dwell - ing.

VERSES:

1. Hear, O Lord, _____ the sound of my call - ing. Hear, O

to REFRAIN

Lord, and show me Your way. _____

2. The Lord is my light, and hope of salvation.
   The Lord is my refuge; whom should I fear?

3. Wait on the Lord, and hope in His mercy.
   Wait on the Lord, and live in His love.

244
Watchman, How Goes The Night?

TEXT: Isaiah 21:13; Matthew 6:10;
Romans 13:12; Revelation 21:3-4.
USE: Time of Advent; Morning Prayer;
Hymn for all times.

♩ = 76

LUCIEN DEISS

ANTIPHON *(Lower notes - Harmony)*

Watch-man, how— goes the night?

Watch-man, how— goes the night?

The night is end-ing; the

day is dawn-ing. We re-turn—to—

serve— the— Lord. The morn-ing

comes and the night fol-lows soon. Let us

walk as child-ren of the light.

Copyright © 1982 by Lucien Deiss. Published exclusively by NALR. 10802 N. 23rd Avo., Phoenix, Arizona 85029. All rights reserved.

VERSES:

1. May the day come when our night
2. May the day come when our hope
3. May the day come when Your love

will meet, O Lord,   Your
will find, O Lord,   Your
will fill, O Lord,   our

light.   May the day come
star.   May the day come
earth.   May the day come

when our tears   will meet, O
when our paths   will reach, O
when Your Church   will find, O

Lord,   Your smile.
Lord,   Your home.
Lord,   Your heav - en.

1.- 3. Let Your King-dom come a-mong us.

(To Antiphon)

Let Your love be near!

245   We Were Strangers

TEXT: Ephesians 2:12-16;
        Galatians 3:28.

USE: Advent; Lent;
        12th Sunday, C; 16th Sunday, B.

♩ = 72   *VERSES: (Lower notes - Harmony)*

LUCIEN DEISS

1. - 3. We were strang - ers, ex - clud - ed

from the prom - ise of the

Cov - e - nant, with - out hope, with-out God in the

world. But You, Je - sus Christ, have

come in our midst. You cre -

ate in Your bod - y one sin -gle new man. You

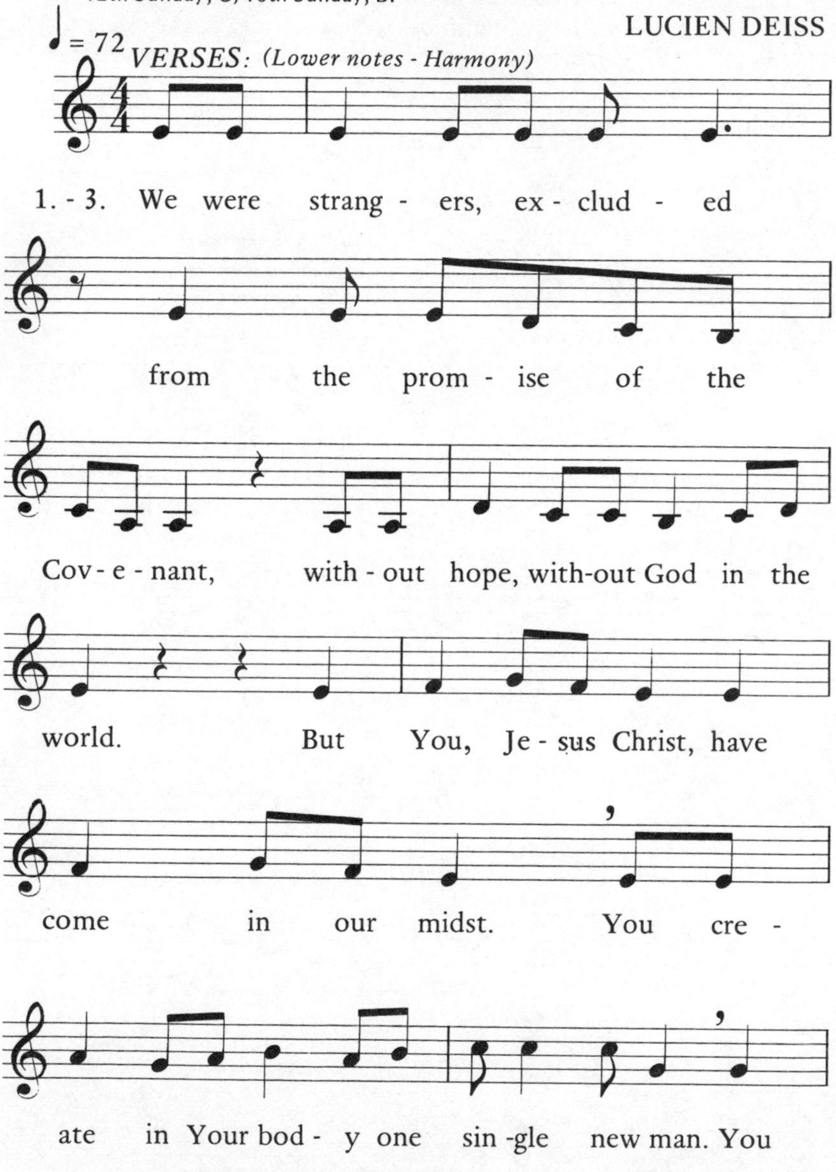

Copyright © 1982 by Lucien Deiss. Published exclusively by NALR. 10802 N. 23rd Ave., Phoenix, Arizona 85029. All rights reserved.

seal our peace by Your cross.

1. In You, ___ men of free - dom and
2. In You, ___ men and wom- en, old
3. Through You, ___ we have ac - cess to

slaves ___ who live in bond - age will
peo - ple and small child - ren will
God, ___ our lov - ing Fa - ther, led

now ___ be ___ broth - ers.
form ___ one ___ bod - y.
by ___ one ___ Spir - it.

ANTIPHON

You have bro - ken down the

bar - ri - er which had di-vid - ed Your

child - ren.   You   have   put to death hos -

til - i - ty,   and

You brought us peace —   in — Your love.

246   Whatsoever You Do

WILLARD F. JABUSCH

REFRAIN

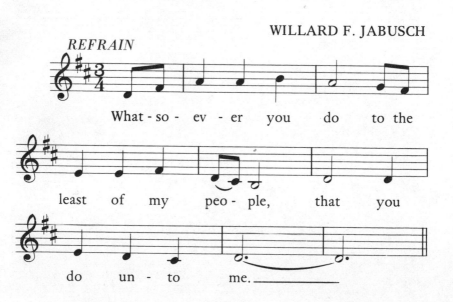

What - so - ev - er   you   do   to the

least   of   my   peo - ple,   that   you

do   un - to   me._____

Copyright ©1966, 1980 by Willard F. Jabusch. Published by NALR,
10802 N. 23rd Ave., Phoenix, AZ 85029. All rights reserved.

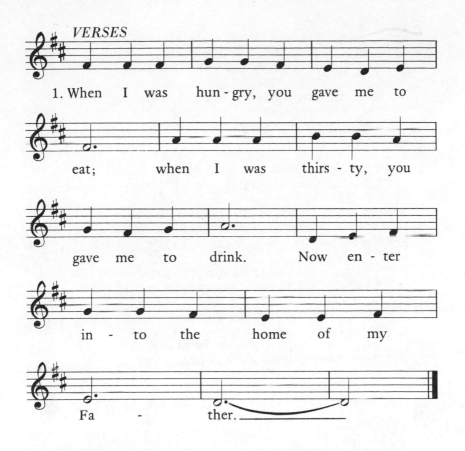

VERSES

1. When I was hun-gry, you gave me to eat; when I was thirs-ty, you gave me to drink. Now en-ter in-to the home of my Fa - ther.

2. When I was homeless, you opened your door;
   When I was naked, you gave me your coat.
   Now enter into the home of my Father.

3. When I was weary, you helped me find rest;
   When I was anxious, you calmed all my fears.
   Now enter into the home of my Father.

4. When I was little, you taught me to read;
   When I was lonely, you gave me your love.
   Now enter into the home of my Father.

5. When in a prison, you came to my cell;
   When on a sick bed, you cared for my needs.
   Now enter into the home of my Father.

6. In a strange country, you made me a home;
   Seeking employment, you found me a job.
   Now enter into the home of my Father.

7. Hurt in a battle, you bound up my wounds;
   Searching for kindness, you held out your hand.
   Now enter into the home of my Father.

8. When I was Black or Latino or White,
   Mocked and insulted, you carried my cross.
   Now enter into the home of my Father.

9. When I was aged, you bothered to smile;
   When I was restless, you listened and cared.
   Now enter into the home of my Father.

10. You saw me covered with spittle and blood;
    You knew my features, though grimy with sweat.
    Now enter into the home of my Father.

11. When I was laughed at, you stood by my side;
    When I was happy, you shared in my joy.
    Now enter into the home of my Father.

247 With Faith Grown in Suffering

REFRAIN   CAREY LANDRY

With faith grown in suf-fer-ing, —

faith grown in pain, we come in our

weak-ness to You; — to You, the

Copyright ©1980 by NALR. 10802 N. 23rd Ave., Phoenix, Arizona 85029.
All rights reserved.

Lord of hope, You, our strength, we
trust, we wait, we be - lieve! _____

VERSES:

1. O God of our praise,
2. O God of our pain,

do not be si - lent,
our dy - ings, our ri - sings,

in Your great love de - li - ver
in You a - lone we find our

to REFRAIN

us. _____
strength. _____

351

248 You Have Searched Our Hearts

CAREY LANDRY

You have searched our hearts, O Lord,

You know us all so well.

You un-der-stand our thoughts, O Lord,

You call us each by name.

VERSE 1:

1. You know when I sit and when I

stand, You know each thing I do.

E - ven be-fore a word is on my lips, ____ You

Copyright ©1982 by NALR. 10802 N. 23rd Ave., Phoenix, Arizona 85029.
All rights reserved.

to REFRAIN

know what I will say. _____

VERSES 2, 3 and 4:

2. You know my com - ings and my

go - ings,_ You are with me wher - ev -er I

go; be - fore me, be - hind me and

all a - round me _____ Your

to REFRAIN

love is too won-der- ful to know. ___

3. Where can I go from Your Spirit?
   From Your presence, where can I flee?
   If I fly to the sunrise or swim beneath the sea,
   Your hand would still be guiding me.

4. You created my in-most self,
   You formed me in my mother's womb.
   I stand in awe at the wonder of my life:
   The wonder of Your love.

249 You Will Draw Water

TOM CONRY

REFRAIN

You will draw wa - ter__ from the
well of the King - dom of God.

You will draw wa - ter__ from the
well of the King - dom of God.

1. God alone is my rock;
   How then should I be afraid?

2. God alone is my strength;
   Who then can stand before me?

3. God alone is my rest;
   The Lord God is my safety.

4. God alone is my peace;
   He shatters steel and nations.

5. God alone is my day;
   His name will shine before me.

6. God alone is my prize;
   Though mountains fall to pieces.

* Editor's Note: *Verses to overlap Refrain, begin here.*

Copyright©1981 by NALR, 10802 N. 23rd Ave., Phoenix, Arizona 85029.
All rights reserved.

250 All I Ask of You

GREGORY NORBET, O.S.B.
Weston Priory

Gently, quietly
REFRAIN

All I ask of you is for-ev-er to re-mem-ber Me ___ as lov-ing you. ___

1-5

Last time

you, ___ for-ev-er as lov-ing ___ you.

Optional

Oo ___

(Fine)

VERSES:

1. Deep the joy of be-ing to-

Copyright©1972, The Benedictine Foundation of the State of Vermont, Inc., Weston, Vermont 05161. Used with permission.

geth - er in one heart and for

to REFRAIN

me that's just ___ where it is.

2. As we make our way through all the joys and pain,
   Can we sense our younger, truer selves?

3. Someone will be calling you to be there for awhile.
   Can you hear their cry from deep within?

4. Laughter, joy and presence: the only gifts you are!
   Have you time? I'd like to be with you.

5. Persons come into the fiber of our lives
   And then their shadow fades and disappears. (But)

251 All Those Who Love Me

John 14:23,24 **(If Anyone Loves Me)**

Gently

GREGORY NORBET, O.S.B.
Weston Priory

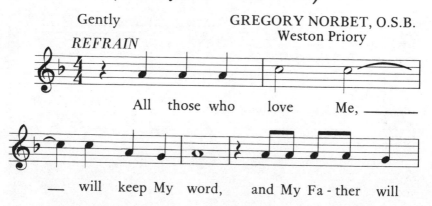

All those who love Me, ___

___ will keep My word, and My Fa - ther will

Copyright©1972, The Benedictine Foundation of the State of Vermont, Inc.,
Weston, Vermont 05161. Used with permission.

love them, _____ and We shall come to them ___

___ and make our home with them.

VERSE:

And My word is not My own:

no, _____ it is the word of the

to REFRAIN

One Who __ sent Me. _____

Anyone Who Eats This Bread 252

GREGORY NORBET, O.S.B.
Weston Priory

With movement and feeling (♩ = 72)

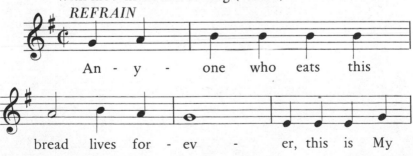

REFRAIN

An - y - one who eats this

bread lives for - ev - er, this is My

Copyright©1974, The Benedictine Foundation of the State of Vermont, Inc.,
Weston, Vermont 05161. Used with permission.

life _____ for the world; _____

— an-y- time you come to-geth-er in My

name I am there with My love _____

— and with My peace. _____

VERSES:

1. This is the bread come down from a-

bove, the food of way-far-ing

Chris - tians, the life of our

broth - er, Je - sus Christ: our

way our light and our deep -

to REFRAIN

- est   peace. _____

2. The poor and the hungry are welcome here
   To share this heavenly banquet;
   Believe in Jesus, God's Word made flesh
   And give your all to this moment of joy.

3. The Christ is born of Mary,
   The promise fulfilled for salvation;
   We bear His name with conviction,
   That everlasting life will be ours.

4. This food endures to eternal life:
   The Christ who is here and has risen.
   We manifest our faith in Him,
   The teacher of all that is good and true.

Be Glad, O People   253

Based on Isaiah 49

GREGORY NORBET, O.S.B.
Weston Priory

Lively, with spirit
VERSES:

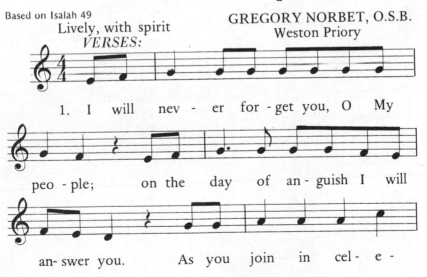

1. I will nev - er for - get you, O My
   peo - ple;   on the   day   of an - guish I will
   an - swer you.   As you   join   in   cel - e -

Copyright©1978, The Benedictine Foundation of the State of Vermont, Inc.,
Weston, Vermont 05161. Used with permission.

bra - tion, My joy will move a - mong you. ____ Be glad, O peo - ple of the earth! Lift up your heart with song and ____ dance, for I am with you, yes with - in you, for - ev - er! you are the heart of My heart. ____

REFRAIN

2. You shall find a land to be your home,
   Where sheep and cattle may freely roam,
   Mountains from which springs shall flow
   With living waters.

3. I will make your faith burn brightly,
   So that others may find life's fullness:
   Freedom for all captives
   And justice for all nations.

4. No longer will the circle of your life,
   Its pain and goodness
   Be just for yourself;
   Your gift to share will flower.

5. As you work for others' freedom,
   With a seed of hope within you,
   Hunger shall not harm you,
   Nor thirst withdraw your courage.

By the Love

Based on Jn. 13:35; 14 and 15

254

GREGORY NORBET, O.S.B.
Weston Priory

Joyfully, with movement

REFRAIN

By the love with which you live ___

___ and the joy that o - ver flows

you will be known as my dis - ci - ples;

To Coda

in that love shall I a - bide.

VERSES:

1. Trust in God and in me; ___ do not be

to REFRAIN

trou - bled, for I am with you.

Coda

in that love shall I a - bide. ___

Copyright©1981, The Benedictine Foundation of the State of Vermont, Inc., Weston, Vermont 05161. Used with permission.

2. You shall follow My path:
   I am the Way and the Truth and Life.

3. Those who keep My word
   Shall have within them the One Who sent Me.

4. Spirit Holy shall you know,
   Revealing wisdom and Truth in My name.

5. From the depth of My heart
   I leave you peace to share with others.

6. No greater love can you have
   Than to give your life for other persons.

7. I now call you My friends;
   The life of God have I shared among you.

8. Only this do I ask:
   Sincerely love and bless each other.

255   A Child Is Born

Lively
REFRAIN

GREGORY NORBET, O.S.B.
Weston Priory

A Child is born to us to-day, Al-le-lu-ia. He is our

Copyright©1971, 1980, The Benedictine Foundation of the State of Vermont, Inc.,
Weston, Vermont 05161. Used with permission.

Sav - ior and our God, Al -

le - lu - ia. _____

Last time only

Al - le - lu - ia. _____

_____ Al - le - lu - ia. _____

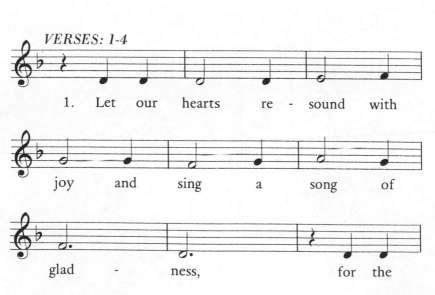

VERSES: 1-4

1. Let our hearts re - sound with

joy and sing a song of

glad - ness, for the

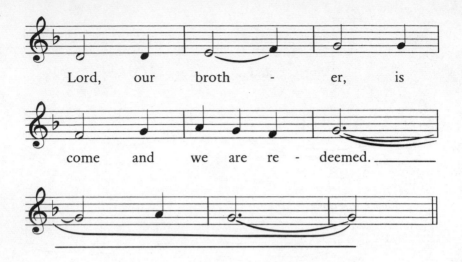

Lord, our broth - er, is

come and we are re - deemed. _____

2. Tell the world of our good news:
   Jesus the Christ is among us,
   And His presence we celebrate
   Offering peace and our joy to all.

3. Christ is born, the Christ is come!
   Sing ev'ryone: Alleluia!
   Caught in wonder at this birth
   We worship God become one with us.

4. Glory to God, born today
   Of the Virgin Mary,
   In a cave at Bethlehem:
   Is there room in our lives for Him?

VERSES: 5-8

5. His name shall be E -

man - u - el: God Who

lives a - mong us.

An - gels sing and shep - herds

cry: born is the Sav - ior, our

Lord.

6. The Magi went and worshipped Him
   With gifts so precious and costly.
   In the fervor of their faith
   They sought the Child Who is Lord and King.

7. The Lord will make integrity
   And peace to grow in our times,
   A covenant He offers us.
   Lasting joy will be ours to share.

8. Arise, shine out, Jerusalem!
   The glory of Yahweh has come to you.
   Lift up your eyes and look around!
   Radiant is your salvation.

256 Choose Life

Based on Deut. 30:20

Gently, with feeling
REFRAIN

GREGORY NORBET, O.S.B.
Weston Priory

Choose life that you — may — be —

— a leav - en for the hu - man fam - i -

ly; _____ then shall you

live — in — peace, _____ as

jus - tice bears the gift of free - dom

through - out all the world. _____

Copyright©1981, The Benedictine Foundation of the State of Vermont, Inc., Weston, Vermont 05161. Used with permission.

VERSES:

1. This is the prom-ise of our God, _____

_____ Whose Spir - it breathes with - in each heart of

flesh, _____ call - ing us

all to live with care _____ for

crea - tures, great and small, for earth, the

to REFRAIN

wa - ters and the air. _____

2. Children of earth, unite and sing
   Of beauty and of truth held in your hands;
   Flowers of hope you are for us,
   As love becomes your bread in life,
   Your life our only hope.

3. Prophets of progress, heed our cry
   And listen to your inner spirit's thirst
   For more of life that shall not die;
   Make clear your choice to live for others
   While there still is time.

257　Come Now, My Love

GREGORY NORBET, O.S.B.
Weston Priory

Moderately fast

Come now, my love, my love-ly one, come. Come now, my love, my love-ly one, come, for see, the win-ter is past, the snows are o-ver and done. The flow-ers ap-pear in the

Copyright©1971, The Benedictine Foundation of the State of Vermont, Inc.,
Weston, Vermont 05161. Used with permission.

fields, the sea - son of joy - ful songs has
come, the coo - ing of the tur - tle dove —
— is heard in our land.
Come now, my love, my love - ly one,
come. Show me your face,
let me hear your voice, for your
voice is sweet and your face so
beau - ti - ful. _____

258 For Us to Live

Based on: Jn. 5:24

GREGORY NORBET, O.S.B.
Weston Priory

With conviction and movement

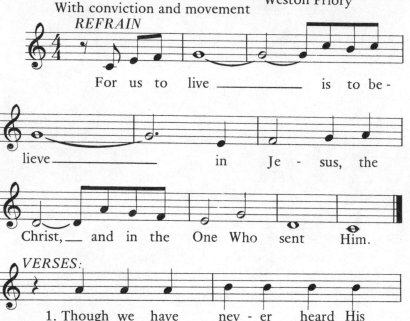

REFRAIN

For us to live ———— is to be-
lieve ———— in Je - sus, the
Christ, — and in the One Who sent Him.

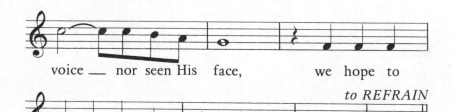

VERSES:

1. Though we have nev - er heard His
voice — nor seen His face, we hope to
let His word take root in our lives. ————

to REFRAIN

2. It is in spirit and in truth that we are known,
   Free to be lifted up in each other's lives.

3. Simply to live for one another as bread:
   This is the call of Jesus stirring within.

Copyright©1978, The Benedictine Foundation of the State of Vermont, Inc.,
Weston, Vermont 05161. Used with permission.

4. It is God's spirit that gives life and not the flesh:
   Yes, Jesus' words, for us, are spirit and life.

5. Nothing can take from us the hope in which we've grown;
   Not even death shall separate us from His love.

6. With inner freedom to be gift with our lives
   No longer shall our days be centered on self.

7. If we should thirst for truth and ask for more life,
   Then shall the spirit waken faith that is real.

Go Up to the Mountain 259

Based on: Isaiah 38 & 40

GREGORY NORBET, O.S.B.
Weston Priory

Brightly, with spirit
REFRAIN

Go up to the moun - tain, joy - ful bear - er of good news; shout with a full _ voice: ___ our God _ is _ near. _____

VERSES:

1. Those who hope in the Lord _ ___ find their strength _ re - newed; _____

Copyright©1978, 1980, The Benedictine Foundation of the State of Vermont, Inc.,
Weston, Vermont 05161. Used with permission.

they soar like an ea - gle;___
like an ea - gle they fly. ___

to REFRAIN

2. Those who hope in the Lord never grow weary
   And never lose heart should they run or walk.

3. See, the Lord is coming, is coming with strength
   Like a shepherd leading the flock.

4. Yahweh, come to us and our harps will resound
   With such gladness all the days of our life.

5. Yes, it is the living, the living who praise You
   And we speak to all of Your faithfulness.

260 The Goodness of God

GREGORY NORBET, O.S.B.
Weston Priory

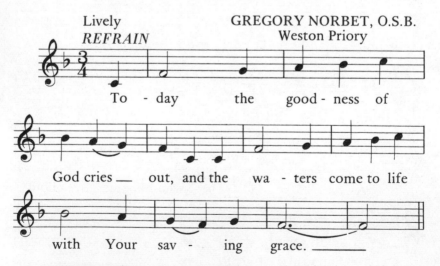

Lively
REFRAIN
To - day the good - ness of
God cries ___ out, and the wa - ters come to life
with Your sav - ing grace. ___

Copyright©1971, 1980, The Benedictine Foundation of the State of Vermont, Inc.,
Weston, Vermont 05161. Used with permission.

1. O Fa - ther of all, You gave us Your Son to re - deem us from the dark - ness — of sin. ___

2. Radiant is Your joy, O God,
And the splendor of Your love is alive, alive.

3. Today You appear, O Christ, to the world
And Your light has shone upon us, O Lord.

Happy Those Who Hear the Word of God   261

Based on Lk. 11:28; Mt. 7:7; 5:15, 16;
Lk. 10:27

Spirited

GREGORY NORBET, O.S.B.
Weston Priory

REFRAIN

Hap - py those who hear the word — of — God and fol - low it — with their lives. ___

Copyright©1979, The Benedictine Foundation of the State of Vermont, Inc.,
Weston, Vermont 05161. Used with permission.

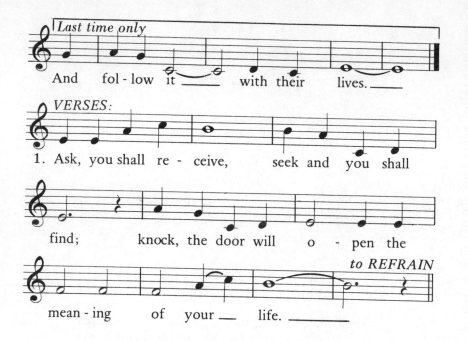

Last time only

And fol-low it ____ with their lives. ____

VERSES:

1. Ask, you shall re - ceive, seek and you shall find; knock, the door will o - pen the

to REFRAIN

mean - ing of your ____ life. ____

2. Leaving all we'd known
   To follow Spirit's call,
   We have found a healing love
   In the sharing of our life.

3. No one lights a lamp
   And hides it from the dark;
   Should we not be free
   In showing compassion in the light?

4. So love the Lord, our God
   With all of our heart;
   Life shall find its fullness
   In loving others as ourselves.

Hosea

Based on Hosea

GREGORY NORBET, O.S.B.
Weston Priory

Gently, with movement
VERSES:

1. Come back to Me ___ with
2. The wil - der - ness ___ will
3. ｛ You shall sleep ___ se -

1. all your heart. ___ Don't let fear ___
2. lead ___ you ___ to your heart ___
3. cure with peace; ___ faith - ful - ness ___

1. ___ keep us a - part. ___
2. ___ where I will speak. ___ In -
3. ___ will be your joy. ___ (to Refrain)

1. Trees do bend, ___ 'though straight and tall; ___
2. teg - ri - ty ___ and jus - tice, ___

1. ___ so must we ___ to
2. ___ with ten - der - ness ___

REFRAIN

1. oth - ers' call. ___ Long have I
2. you shall know. ___

Copyright©1972, The Benedictine Foundation of the State of Vermont, Inc.,
Weston, Vermont 05161. Used with permission.

waited for your coming home to Me and
living deeply our new life.

263 Journeys Ended, Journeys Begun

GREGORY NORBET, O.S.B.
Weston Priory

Chanted, with movement
REFRAIN

Journeys ended, journeys begun: to go where we have never been, to be beyond our past, moments of lifting up, transcending death,

Copyright©1977, The Benedictine Foundation of the State of Vermont, Inc.,
Weston, Vermont 05161. Used with permission.

ris - ing in trans - par - ent light to the

full - ness of God's — pres - ence.

Al - le - lu - ia, — Al - le -

lu - ia, — Al - le - lu - ia.

VERSES :

1. Do not let your hearts be trou - bled:

trust in God and trust in Me, you shall not be a-

lone. — To pre -pare a place for you I

rit.   *a tempo*

go but shall re - turn so that you may

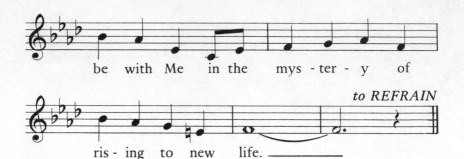

be with Me in the mys - ter - y of

to REFRAIN

ris - ing to new life. _____

2. Loving one another in truth,
   Choosing clear the many deaths
   Of going beyond self,
   Living in the Spirit
   Of One Who gave His life
   So that we might come to know
   How profound the gift of God in Jesus Christ.

3. There can be no greater love than this:
   To give our lives for others:
   Our joy will be complete.
   I have told you all this
   So that you may find peace
   In the sharing of your life
   And know the depth of love to which we're called.

The Lord Jesus 264

GREGORY NORBET, O.S.B.
Weston Priory

Meditative, with movement
REFRAIN

The Lord — Je - sus, af -ter eat - ing with His friends, washed their feet and said to them: Do you know what I your Lord, have done to you? ___ I have giv - en you ex - am - ple, ___ that so you al - so should do. ___

Copyright©1972, The Benedictine Foundation of the State of Vermont, Inc.,
Weston, Vermont 05161. Used with permission.

VERSES:

1. You are my friends:
a
(and
man can have no great - er love than to
you)

to REFRAIN

give his life for his friends.
(your) (your)

2. Peace I leave with you,
   My peace I give to all
   Who live with sincere love for ev'ryone.

3. I am the vine
   And you, the branch: remain in Me
   And you will bear abundant fruit.

4. Those who come to Me
   Will never thirst nor want for food
   And I will raise them up on the last day.

The Lord's Prayer 265

GREGORY NORBET, O.S.B.
Weston Priory

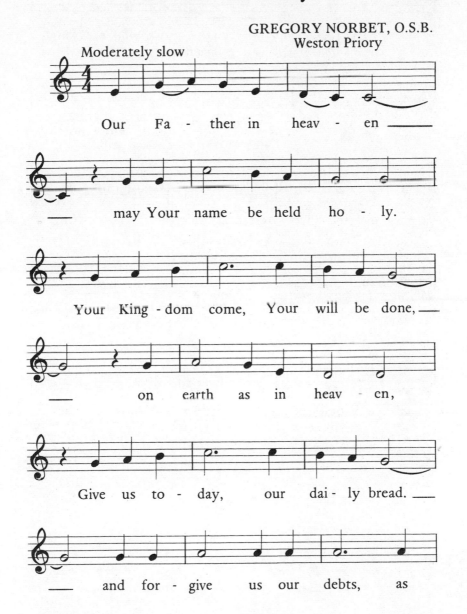

Our Fa - ther in heav - en ___
___ may Your name be held ho - ly.
Your King - dom come, Your will be done, ___
___ on earth as in heav - en,
Give us to - day, our dai - ly bread. ___
___ and for - give us our debts, as

Copyright©1972, 1975, The Benedictine Foundation of the State of Vermont, Inc., Weston, Vermont 05161. Used with permission.

we have for - giv - en those who are in

debt to us. And do not

put us to the test _____ but

save ___ us, _____ from the e -

vil one. _____ For Yours is ⸱ the

King - dom, the pow- er and the glo - ry, for -

ev - er. _____ A - men. _____

My Friends, I Bless You 266

Lively
REFRAIN

GREGORY NORBET, O.S.B.
Weston Priory

My friends, I bless __ you and give you My joy, _____ as I go to pre - pare a place for you. _____

VERSES:

1. Do not be anx - ious and with - out joy, ___ e - ven

Copyright©1974, 1977, The Benedictine Foundation of the State of Vermont, Inc.,
Weston, Vermont 05161. Used with permission.

though I am leav - ing your

midst. I shall re - main in your heart if

on - ly you will let Me, if

to REFRAIN

on - ly you will let Me.

2. If you love Me you will be happy to know
That I shall be at peace
In the Father's presence and with all those
Whom I have ever loved.

3. Peace I leave with you, My friends,
Peace the world cannot give.
My Spirit shall remain among you,
Bringing My words to life.

4. Trust in God and trust in Me;
Do not live in fear.
In My Father's house there is room for ev'ryone.
There shall be a place for you.

5. If you keep My Word and live in My love,
Your joy will be complete.
By the love you have for others
All will know you are My friends.

Something Which Is Known 267

Based on 1 John 1

GREGORY NORBET, O.S.B.
Weston Priory

Gently, with movement

1. Some-thing which is known to have been from the be - gin - ning: this we have heard and seen with our own eyes. Some - thing we have touched and have care - ful - ly watched: the Word, Who is life, this we share with you.

2. This is the life of our God the light so gra - cious, word be - come flesh: there is no great-er won - der All that we have wit - nessed be - came — new vi - sion this our hope for you, a - live in God's own spir - it,

3. He it is in whom we have found the light of truth, — source of our hope, a - bid - ing gift of God's love. Through that love we pass and are born in life un - end - ing: Jesus, our Lord, the full - ness of our joy.

Copyright©1978, 1980, The Benedictine Foundation of the State of Vermont, Inc.,
Weston, Vermont 05161. Used with permission.

Al - le - lu - ia, ___
Al - le - lu - ia, Al - le
lu - ia, ___ Al - le -

Last time - repeat REFRAIN

lu - ia. ___

2. This is the life of our God, so gracious, word become flesh:
   There is no greater wonder.
   All that we have witnessed became new vision:
   This our hope for you, alive in God's own spirit.

3. He it is in Whom we have found the light of truth,
   Source of our hope, abiding gift of God's love.
   Through that love we pass and are born in life unending:
   Jesus, our Lord, the fullness of our joy.

Song of the Prophet 268

Based on: Jer. 1:5-10; Is. 6:6-7; 61:1-3; 25:1

GREGORY NORBET, O.S.B.
Weston Priory

With movement and feeling

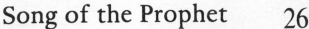

VERSES:

1. " Be - fore your birth, be - fore I formed you in your moth - er's womb,"

says the word of the Lord, _____ " I have con - se - crat - ed

you to be a proph - et who will speak My name through - out all the _

world."

Copyright©1981, The Benedictine Foundation of the State of Vermont, Inc., Weston, Vermont 05161. Used with permission.

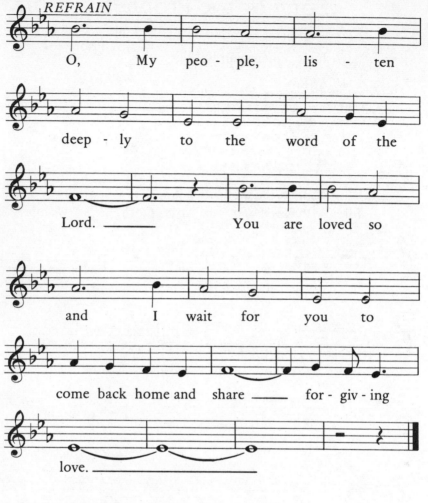

REFRAIN

O, My peo - ple, lis - ten deep - ly to the word of the Lord. _____ You are loved so and I wait for you to come back home and share _____ for - giv - ing love. _____

2. Lord, I am but a child,
   I do not know what I should say!
   "Do not be afraid.
   I am with you and My words shall burn
   As coals within your mouth;
   Let all nations hear."

3. Even though the poor cry out
   My people do not heed their tears
   And they turn away;
   As injustice comes to fruit
   In violence within ev'ry land,
   The human heart grows weak.

4. The Spirit of the Lord, our God,
   Has anointed me to share good news with the poor,
   To bind and bring together
   All broken, lonely lives
   Those who await new hope.

5. Proclaim a year of blessing
   From Yahweh, our God,
   This is the Word of the Lord;
   And to those held captive
   In their chains of spirit and of flesh:
   Give them freedom's joy!

6. No longer shall the mournful
   Dwell in their tears;
   Give them gladness
   To see the beauty of the one
   Whose life is but their ev'ry breath:
   Now let sorrow flee!

7. In You, O God, my heart is glad
   As freely as I live
   In Your saving love;
   To know the presence of Your Word
   Within my ev'ry hope:
   Let this vision now live.

269   Spirit of God

GREGORY NORBET, O.S.B.
Weston Priory

With movement

REFRAIN

Spir - it of God, be for us joy. Heal - ing gift of

Last time to Coda

love, cre - at - ing a new heart. ____

Long- ing to be Spir - it a -

live, ver - y life of

God, be root - ed with - in us. ____

Copyright©1977, The Benedictine Foundation of the State of Vermont, Inc.,
Weston, Vermont 05161. Used with permission.

VERSES:

1. Voice which calls us be - yond scat - tered dreams, bar - ren days to re - ceive and give of God's love. _____

to REFRAIN

Coda

Heal - ing gift of love cre - at - ing a new heart. _____

2. May You kindle our hope in the morning of life;
   May You bring us peace with each day's end.

3. In the silence of prayer inner freedom will sing
   Of more being, vision and truth.

4. 'Though exalted, our hopes no less real shall they be;
   In compassion faithfulness thrives.

5. We've been waiting so long for this moment in life,
   For the fullness of brothers'/sisters' love.

270 The Sun Is Rising

GREGORY NORBET, O.S.B.
Weston Priory

With spirit
VERSES:

1. Let the pain of our strug - gle for free - dom be en - dured with all the strength of our lives. With the dawn ___ shall come our de - liv' - rance from the pow - er of greed ___ and of wealth.

Copyright©1976, 1977, The Benedictine Foundation of the State of Vermont, Inc.,
Weston, Vermont 05161. Used with permission.

REFRAIN

The sun is ris - ing, _____ free - dom is com - ing _____ hope soon shall flow - er _____

1. _____ in the birth _ of jus - tice.

2. _____ with jus - tice for all. _____

2. If the seed falls into the ground,
   And should it die, it can only spring up
   With new life that nourishes others:
   What a beautiful sign of God's love!

3. Thirsting for a love that unites
   And can heal lives broken with pain
   We are sure to live with God's Spirit
   When we give without thought of gain.

4. With forgiveness we've found new meaning
   And a gift to be offered to those
   Who have been so long our oppressors:
   Understanding and the challenge to love.

5. Sing a song that rings with thanksgiving:
   Alleluia! Alleluia!
   We have all received of God's fullness
   In the rising of Jesus to life.

271 That There May Be Bread

GREGORY NORBET, O.S.B.
Weston Priory

Moderately
REFRAIN

That there may be bread, that there may be joy for all hu- man-i-ty to share ___ with gra-ti- tude: let this be our prayer, and may each child of earth long for a free-dom that will flour-ish in all lands.

Copyright©1979, The Benedictine Foundation of the State of Vermont, Inc.,
Weston, Vermont 05161. Used with permission

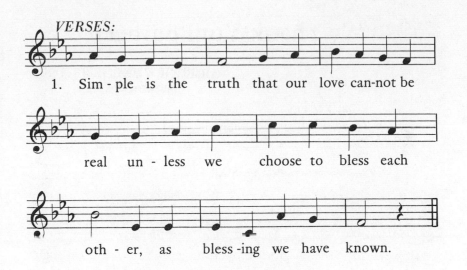

1. Sim-ple is the truth that our love can-not be
real un-less we choose to bless each
oth-er, as bless-ing we have known.

2. Still, the long night falls
And yet for some, deep hunger cries
As their tears become their bread:
Their hope too soon may die.

3. Lord, what should I do
To have eternal life?
Love the God who lives within you
And your neighbor as yourself.

4. Lord, who is my neighbor?
The one whose struggle
And whose needs you overlook,
While your own comfort you secure.

5. Grateful for our life,
Can we be free to thirst and work
For the planting and the harvest
Of Kingdom's life in all?

6. At this table of thanksgiving
We are fed
With the life of Jesus risen,
In whom our hope is born.

7. Sign of God's deep love
Is this banquet of new life:
Know the presence of the Holy,
In spirit and in truth.

272   We Thank You, Father

GREGORY NORBET, O.S.B.
Weston Priory

Moderately

REFRAIN

We thank You Fa - ther, _____ _____ for the gift of faith, _____ through Je - sus Christ Your Son, and for the gift of life _____ with each oth - er, _____ in this _____ _____ our fam - i - ly. May Your Good _ News _____ be a con - stant source _____

Copyright©1971, The Benedictine Foundation of the State of Vermont, Inc.,
Weston, Vermont. 05161. Used with permission.

of strength and joy,

for ___ all of us ____ who

share __ in ____ Your won - der - ful

VERSE:

love __ each day. ____ To

live in the Spir - it is to

grow in li - ber - ty. With - out

to REFRAIN

love our free - dom can - not be real.

273 Wherever You Go

GREGORY NORBET, O.S.B.
Weston Priory

Moderately Slow

Wher-ev - er you go ____ I shall go. ____ Wher - ev - er you live ____ so shall I live. ____ Your peo - ple will be my peo - ple, and your God ____ will be my God, too. ____ Wher - ev - er you die ____

Copyright©1972, The Benedictine Foundation of the State of Vermont, Inc., Weston, Vermont 05101. Used with permission.

I shall die, ___ and there shall
I be bur-ied be-side you. ___
We will be to-geth-er ___ for-
ev - er, and our love ___ will be the
gift of our life. ___

(Spoken:)
I want to say something to all of you
Who have become a part
Of the fabric of my life.

The color and texture
Which you have brought into my being
Have become a song,
And I want to sing it forever.

There is an energy in us
Which makes things happen
When the paths of other persons
Touch ours
And we have to be there
And let it happen.

When the time
Of our particular sunset comes
Our thing, our accomplishment
Won't really matter a great deal.

But the clarity and care
With which we have loved others
Will speak with vitality
Of the great gift of life
We have been for each other.

Gregory Norbet O.S.B.

Copyright©1972, The Benedictine Foundation of the State of Vermont, Inc.,
Weston, Vermont 05161. Used with permission.

274 Witnesses

Based on: Ex. 3:8, 12; 15:2
Mt. 25:35; 18:21f; 10:39
Lk. 14:27; 1 Cor. 13:1f

GREGORY NORBET, O.S.B.
Weston Priory

With conviction and feeling

REFRAIN

Wit - ness - es of dy - ing and of ris - ing: these mar - tyrs who live the Good News of Je - sus ris - en. Spir - it calls to heed their voice, their mes - sage: trans - form all __ fear with jus - tice and com - pas - sion. ____

VERSES:

1. As you lead your peo - ple to the

Copyright©1981, The Benedictine Foundation of the State of Vermont, Inc.,
Weston, Vermont 05101. Used with permission.

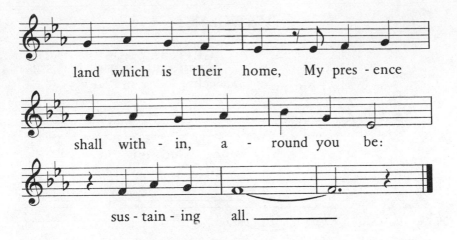

land which is their home, My pres-ence
shall with-in, a-round you be:
sus-tain-ing all. _____

2. I shall be your strength, your song,
   Your courage as you free
   All those held captive by injustice
   And others' greed.

3. Feed the hungry, clothe the homeless,
   Nurture broken lives;
   In the sharing of your humanness
   God's love abounds.

4. Lord, how often shall we forgive
   Those who do harm; seven times?
   No, I say seventy,
   And even more.

5. Break all unjust structures
   As you share your daily bread
   With those working for their freedom
   And joy of life.

6. If you will not carry your own cross
   And follow Me,
   You shall not be My disciple
   For others.

7. Those possessed by power's comfort
   Live in emptiness;
   But those who give their lives in My name
   Will birth new hope.

8. Though the gifts of knowledge
   And of preaching strengthen us,
   Unless we live with compassion
   What shall remain?

275   Yahweh

Based on Is. 12:2, 3

GREGORY NORBET, O.S.B.
Weston Priory

Copyright©1972, The Benedictine Foundation of the State of Vermont, Inc.,
Weston, Vermont 05161. Used with permission.

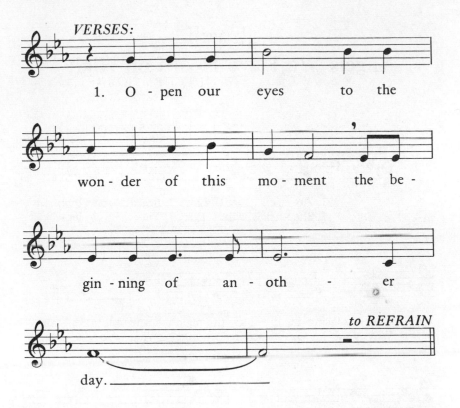

2. Be with us, Lord, as we break through with each other
   To find the truth and beauty of each friend.

3. When ev'ning comes and our day of toil is over
   Give us rest, O Lord, in the joy of many friends.

4. Take us beyond the vision of this day to
   The deep and wide ways of Your infinite love and life.

Angels We Have Heard on High

Traditional French
Arr. by Henry Papale

1. An - gels we have heard on high
2. Shep-herds, why this ju - bi - lee?

Sweet - ly sing- ing   o'er the plains, And the moun-tains
Why your joy-ous   strains pro-long? What the glad-some

in re- ply   Ech - o - ing their joy - ous strains.
ti - dings bring Which in - spire your heav'n- ly song?

Glo - - - - - - ri -a

1.   **2.**

in ex -cel -sis De - o; De - o.

Arrangements and additional lyrics.
©1980 NALR, 10802 N. 23rd Ave., Phoenix, Arizona 85029, All rights reserved.

Deck the Hall

Arr. by Henry Papale

Arrangements and additional lyrics.
©1980 NALR, 10802 N. 23rd Ave., Phoenix, Arizona 85029. All rights reserved.

The First Nowell

Arr. by Henry Papale

1. The first Nowell the angel did
2. They looked up and saw a great

say Was to cer-tain poor shep-herds in fields as they
star Shin-ing in the east be-yond them

lay; In fields where they lay, keep-ing their
far, And to the earth it gave great

sheep, On a cold win-ter's night that was so
light, And so it con-tin-ued both day and

deep. }
night. } Now-ell, Now-ell, Now-ell, Now-

ell. Born is the King of Is - ra - el.

Arrangements and additional lyrics.

©1980 NALR, 10802 N. 23rd Ave., Phoenix, Arizona 85029, All rights reserved.

God Rest You Merry, Gentlemen

Words by Charles Wesley

Arr. by Henry Papale

Arrangements and additional lyrics.
©1980 NALR, 10802 N. 23rd Ave., Phoenix, Arizona 85029. All rights reserved.

Hark! the Herald Angels Sing

FELIX MENDELSSOHN
Arr. by Henry Papale

1. Hark! the her - ald an - gels sing___
2. Christ, by high - est heav'n a - dored,___

Glo - ry to the new-born King; Peace on earth and
Christ, the ev - er - last - ing Lord, Late in time be -

mer - cy mild,___ God and sin - ners re - con-ciled:
hold him come___ Off - spring of a vir - gin's womb:

Joy - ful all ye na-tions rise,___ Join the tri - umph
Veiled in flesh the God-head see,___ Hail th'in-car - nate

of the skies,___ With th'an - gel - ic host pro- claim,
De - i - ty! ___ Pleased as man with man to dwell,

Christ is___ born in Beth -le -hem.}
Je - sus,___ our Em - man - u - el. } Hark! the her - ald

an - gels sing Glo - ry___ to the new - born King.

Arrangements and additional lyrics.

©1980 NALR, 10802 N. 23rd Ave., Phoenix, Arizona 85029. All rights reserved.

Joy to the World

G.F. HANDEL
Arr. by Henry Papale

1. Joy to the world! the Lord is come: Let earth re - ceive her King; _____ Let ev - 'ry _____ heart _____ pre - pare _____ him _____ room, _____ And heav'n and na - ture _____ sing, And _____ heav'n and na - ture _____ sing, And _____ heav'n _____ and _____ heav'n _____ and na - ture sing.

2. Joy to the world! the Sa - viour reigns: Let men their songs em - ploy, _____ While fields and _____ floods, _____ rocks, hills, _____ and _____ plains, _____ Re - peat the sound - ing _____ joy, Re - peat the sound - ing _____ joy, Re - peat, _____ re - peat _____ the sound - ing joy.

3. He rules the world with truth and grace, And makes the na - tions prove _____ The glo - ries _____ of _____ his right - eous - ness, _____ And won - ders of his _____ love, And _____ won - ders of his _____ love, And _____ won - ders, won - ders of his love.

Arrangements and additional lyrics.

©1980 NALR, 10802 N. 23rd Ave., Phoenix, Arizona 85029. All rights reserved.

O Come, All Ye Faithful

Arr. by Henry Papale

1. O come, all ye faith - ful, Joy - ful and tri - um - phant, O come ye, O come _ ye to Beth - le - hem; Come and be - hold him; Born the King of an - gels.
2. _ Sing, choirs of an - gels, Sing in ex - ul - ta - tion, O sing, all ye ci - ti - zens of heav'n _ a - bove; Glo - ry to God, _ Glo - ry in the high - est.
3. _ Yea, Lord we greet thee, Born this hap - py morn - ing; _ Je - sus, to thee _ be all glo - ry giv'n; Word of the Fa - ther, Now in flesh ap - pear - ing.

O come, let us a - dore him, O come, let us a - dore him, O come, let us a - dore him, _ Christ _ the Lord.

Arrangements and additional lyrics.
©1980 NALR, 10802 N. 23rd Ave., Phoenix, Arizona 85029. All rights reserved.

Silent Night

FRANZ GRUBER
Arr. by Henry Papale

1. Si - lent night, ho - ly night,
2. Si - lent night, ho - ly night,
3. Si - lent night, ho - ly night,

All is calm, all is bright Round yon vir - gin
Shep-herds quake at the sight, Glo - ries stream_ from
Son of God, love's pure light Ra - diant beams_ from

moth - er and child. Ho - ly in - fant so
heav - en a far, Heav'n - ly hosts____ sing
thy ho - ly face, With the dawn of re -

ten - der and mild, Sleep in heav - en - ly
al - le - lu - ia; Christ, the Sav - iour is
deem - ing grace, Je - sus, Lord, at thy

peace, Sleep_ in heav - en - ly peace.
born! Christ_ the Sav -iour is born!
birth, Je - sus, Lord, at thy birth.

Arrangements and additional lyrics.

©1980 NALR, 10802 N. 23rd Ave., Phoenix, Arizona 85029. All rights reserved.

What Child Is This?

Arr. by Henry Papale

1. What child is this, __ who laid to rest, __ On
2. So bring him in - cense, gold and myrrh, __ All

Mar - y's lap __ is sleep - ing? Whom an - gels greet __ with
tongues and peo - ples own __ him. The King of kings __ sal-

an - thems sweet, While shep - herds watch __ are keep - ing?
va - tion brings, Let ev - 'ry heart __ en-throne him.

This, this _____ is Christ the King, _____ Whom
Raise, raise _____ your song on high, _____ While

shep - herds wor-ship and an - gels sing: Haste, haste __ to
Mar - y sings __ a lull - a - by. Joy, joy __ for

bring him praise, __ The babe, __ the son __ of Mar - y.
Christ is born, __ The babe, __ the son __ of Mar - y.

Arrangements and additional lyrics.

©1980 NALR, 10802 N. 23rd Ave., Phoenix, Arizona 85020. All rights reserved.

Indices

(Titles Listed Alphabetically)

418

(List of Songs by Composer)

Song Number, Title

Ault, Gary

82	All That We Have
112	Let All the Earth
123	My Soul Rejoices
236	Sing Alleluia, Sing
146	Speak, Lord

Balhoff, Mike

175	Alleluia
180	Awake, O Sleeper
182	Beatitudes
183	Beginning Today
189	Come, My Children
193	Give Us Living Water
197	He Has Anointed Me
203	I Am the Resurrection
204	I Long for You
216	Lord, Send Out Your Spirit
118	Lord, Today
123	My Soul Rejoices
226	Path of Life
229	Praised Be the Father
134	Remember Your Love
141	Sing to the Lord
242	There Is One Lord
154	We Praise You

Brown, Grayson

110	Jesus, the Bread of Life

Camarata, Tutti, arranger

221	My People

Ceasar, Buddy

97	Emmanuel
123	My Soul Rejoices
136	Service

Chaumont, James

148	Suffering Servant Song

Cohen, Sheldon

192	Gifts for Our Lord

Conry, Tom

83	Anthem
84	Ashes
169	Anamnesis I
170	Anamnesis II
217	Lord, to Whom Shall We Go?
225	Our Life and Our Song
249	You Will Draw Water

Daigle, Gary

175	Alleluia
180	Awake, O Sleeper
189	Come, My Children
193	Give Us Living Water
197	He Has Anointed Me
203	I Am the Resurrection
204	I Long for You
216	Lord, Send Out Your Spirit
118	Lord, Today
226	Path of Life
229	Praised Be the Father
134	Remember Your Love
141	Sing to the Lord
242	There Is One Lord
154	We Praise You

Deiss, Lucien, C.S.Sp.

176	Alleluia, People of God
177	Alleluia, Your Word
179	At All Times
181	Awaken, My Heart
185	The Bread of Rejoicing
190	The Dawn of Day
195	Hail, Holy Queen
199	Holy, Holy, Holy Lord
200	The House Built on the Rock
201	How Beautiful on the Mountains
205	I Saw the Living Water
207	In Those Days
209	Jesus Christ Is Lord
211	The Kingdom of God
212	Lamb of God
213	Let the Earth Resound
218	The Love of God
230	Praised Be the Flower
240	The Song of the Beatitudes
244	Watchman, How Goes the Night?
245	We Were Strangers

Ducote, Darryl

175	Alleluia
116	All Our Joy
180	Awake, O Sleeper

420

Ducote Darryl, (Contd.)

Norbet Gregory O.S.B (Contd)